The Art of Healthy Eating - Savory

Maria Emmerich

These boys are my **inspiration.**

FAMILY is one of God's masterpieces....to be intimate with ones we would have never introduced ourselves to, had they not been placed in our lives.

Thank You

I once heard someone say, "If you want to hear God laugh, tell him what you have planned!" That statement couldn't have been more true for the past few years of my life. I was a planner, and the more I tried to control how things happened, the more frustrated I got. My husband lost his job, my job as a rock-climbing guide didn't pay the bills and we struggled to start our family. All of these trials helped inspire my nutrition business. Throughout this journey I have been able to befriend some amazing people that I need to thank.

Rebecca: I remember meeting you for the first time in Body Pump! Your talent as an artist is amazing! Thank you for all your support and encouragement. This book layout is all Rebecca!

Micah and Kai: We were always meant to be together. I know it sounds crazy, but we are "soul-mates." Micah will do something and Craig will look at me and say, "Oh my, he takes after you!" And Kai is quiet like me with a passion for being outdoors with nature. My life is so full with them in my life. My "Ideal Day" is cooking for them in the kitchen all day and hearing, "Mommy, try."

Jamie: I remember when you first approached me, "Maria, I love your book, but you need a new cover!" Your photography is indescribable! Thank you for the covers of all of my books! I also want to thank you for helping me start my blog; it helped me get up in the morning when I was going through the most difficult time in my life!

Craig: To my love and best friend. Without your technical skills, patience, editing, encouragement and APPETITE, none of this would have happened. SHMILY.

Table of Contents

Information and Recipes in Order of Sequence

Table of Contents

Information and Recipes in Order of Sequence

I grew up with a passion for sports as well as food; my body shape revealed my two loves. I was athletic yet fat. How to lose weight was a complicated puzzle for me, but once I found the right pieces to fit the 'hormone puzzle', it became easy. I learned the secrets of the hormone insulin and the lesser known hormone leptin, that by adopting a very low-glycemic, high-fat (not just high-protein) diet, I had re-sensitized my biochemistry to these essential hormones, which turn off severe food cravings. Best of all, my diet makeover required a lot less self-deprivation than previous diets that didn't stimulate weight loss. The nutrient-rich, relatively high-fat dietary approach I have developed for myself incorporates exotic, little-known replacements for high-glycemic, starchy foods. This philosophy finally gave me total peace with food; something I never imagined possible. The weight came off, even more than my original goal. Included in this book are exotic, tasty, weight loss foods. The love-hate relationship with food typically starts with innocent dieting and calorie counting, followed by out of control bingeing that causes dangerous extremes, such as skipping meals, obsessive-compulsive exercise, and purging. No wonder food becomes the enemy and we become increasingly frustrated and unhappy as we fight the daily battle. I help clients discover that through proper nutrition education, including how to choose the right foods, they can live a life free from cravings and weight gain.

Before my revelation of the biochemistry of food and our weight, I was so proud of my "perfect" diet of whole grains, fruits, and fat-free desserts, but I was still puzzled why I had uncontrollable food cravings. By finding the correct supplements to change my biochemical imbalances, I started a high healthy-fat, grain-free, no-starch diet; I finally found peace in my body. I didn't feel deprived or compelled to overeat.

The 'secret' is to control leptin and insulin hormones. Any diet that stops blood sugar and insulin spikes also allows the cells to regain sensitivity to the noteworthy anti-aging, weight and hunger-regulating hormone called leptin. The hardest part is to remove my clients' fear of fat, because it is almost impossible to obtain this effect without significant amounts of fat in the diet. High protein alone doesn't work because excess protein will also turn to sugar. Low fat, high protein diets will fail to keep your blood sugar from spiking, and will not allow your leptin hormone to increase. Ron Rosedale, MD, author of The Rosedale Diet and a pioneering scientist on the hormone leptin, states, "If you don't get enough fat, you will likely eat too much protein, which then turns to sugar." Do you know what a normal blood sugar level is? 1 cup? 2 cups? NO, 1 TEASPOON of sugar is a normal blood sugar for adults, children, teens and babies. Blood sugar increases insulin and insulin is TOXIC to our bodies and cells.

Insulin and its counterbalancing hormone, glucagon, are in charge of controlling metabolism. The word insulin may immediately call up an association with diabetes, which is totally valid. Controlling blood sugar is insulin's most important job. Many people with heart disease, high cholesterol, diabetes and high blood pressure in their families have inherited a tendency for their insulin sensors on the cells to malfunction because of years of high sugar and starch consumption. As these sensors become tired, insulin resistance develops. Since it's essential to get the sugar out of the blood and into the cells, the pancreas overcompensates by making more and more insulin to force the tired sensors to work. This starts a detrimental cycle of needing ever more insulin to keep the process going. Some people become so resistant to insulin that the amount necessary to make the sensors respond and clear the sugar from the blood is more than their pancreas can make; that person becomes diabetic.

Excess insulin causes a variety of other detrimental problems: it increases the production of cholesterol in the liver, thickens the walls of the arteries, "causing high blood pressure"; the kidneys retain salt and fluid, and it tells our fat cells to store excess starch and sugar.

Insulin's actions are countered by glucagon. Glucagon alerts the liver to slow down triglyceride and cholesterol production, tells the kidneys to release excess salt and fluid, the artery wall to relax and lower blood pressure, and the fat cells to release stored fat to be burned for energy. Insulin, however, is a stronger hormone than glucagon and when it is high, it suppresses glucagon's actions. After a childhood of sugar and starch consumption, metabolic syndrome and insulin resistance happens.

What we eat controls the production of these hormones. This book will teach you how to stimulate glucagon by keeping insulin low, which will allow the metabolism to heal and the malfunctioning sensors to regain sensitivity. Once this healing occurs, the metabolic disturbances caused by elevated insulin will improve or disappear; cholesterol and triglycerides will return to normal, blood pressure returns to normal, blood sugar will stabilize and you will achieve a normal body weight. There's no need to spend huge amounts of money on medications for band-aid "solutions." The affirmative testimonies of my clients support the fact that nutrition is key to a healthy body. You can pay the doctor or you can pay the farmer.

In Gary Taubes book, Why We Get Fat and What To Do About It, a very interesting study conducted by the National Institute of Health, had 20,000 women who were very overweight go on a low calorie diet. On average, the women consumed 360 calories a day less on their diets than they did when they first agreed to participate. If obesity is caused by overeating, then these women were "under-eating" by 360 calories/day. They ate 20% less calories than what the public-health agencies tell us women should eat. The result? After 8 years, the women lost an average of 2 pounds each! AND their waist circumference increased! Which demonstrates that the women didn't lose fat, they lost muscle. This is why a calorie isn't a calorie! A pound of fat contains 3500 calories. Eating 360 calories less everyday should have had the women lose 2 pounds of fat in the first 2 weeks and more than 36 pounds in the first year!

It is all about WHAT we eat rather than how much. Our bodies create biological responses to everything we consume! Choosing the right foods at the right time is an art.

This book is for everyone who has been frustrated with how they look and feel. Maybe you look great, but your health is suffering because you don't have a sense of well-being. Nutrition is fundamental to our health and ability to function at the optimum level daily. I love feeling energetic and confident and desire the same for you! Constant deprivation and guilt regarding food made me miserable. Proper nutrition freed me from that vicious cycle and it will do the same for you, with healthy eating habits and enjoy real food with miraculous benefits.

Check out the delicate Sushi on page 121. You won't believe how simple it is to make and how wonderful it tastes!

Do You Love Sushi?
See page 121

Specific Ingredients

Many everyday food ingredients are very high in sugar and carbs. These tables show the various substitutions I use in my recipes. Use this chart to understand the healthier alternatives and why I have selected various ingredients.

MASHED POTATOES Substitute: Cauliflower for potatoes

Steam some fresh or frozen cauliflower. Then add a dash of butter to the cauliflower, add a little chicken broth or heavy cream, and puree in a food processor or blender. To make it even better, try adding roasted garlic, cheese, or sour cream to the mixture. If you are apprehensive about your family liking this, just substitute ½ the potatoes for cauliflower the first time and see if anyone says anything!

Carbohydrates Eliminated: 30 g per cup
The Taste Test: "After a couple of bites, you forget it's not potatoes."

Potato Substitutions (Per Cup)					
Item	Rating	Carbs	Sugars	Fiber	Calories
Potato	Bad	28	2	4	116
Sweet Potato	Bad	27	6	4	114
Kamucha Squash (NOT Butternut)	OK	7	3	1	30
Pumpkin (for sweet potato)	OK	7.5	1.6	0.6	30
Turnips	OK	8	5	2	36
Jicama	OK	11	2	6	46
Daikon Radish	Best	2	0	0.5	30
Cauliflower	Best	3	1	1	28

RICE Substitute: Cauliflower Rice instead of white rice

Process fresh cauliflower with a food processor until it is the size of rice. Pan fry the "rice" in a dash of butter. Don't add water; cauliflower absorbs water like crazy, and the "granules" will become gummy. To keep it fluffy, just let the moisture in the cauliflower do its work. Great for Mexican dishes, Asian dishes…kids even like it.

Carbs Eliminated: 32 g per cup
The Taste: "Awesome, I like it better than white rice!"

Rice Substitutions (Per Cup)					
Item	Rating	Carbs	Sugars	Fiber	Calories
White Rice	Bad	53	0	0	242
Brown Rice	Bad	46	0	4	218
Quinoa	Bad	39	0	5	222
Wild Rice	Bad	35	1.2	3	166
Cauliflower Rice	Best	3	1	1	28
Miracle Rice	Best	0	0	0	0

PASTA Substitute: spaghetti squash for spaghetti OR fresh shredded ZUCCHINI

Cooked spaghetti squash is Mother Nature's pasta. Squash has a flesh that has noodle-like strands. Cut the squash in half and remove the seeds. Then place each half (cut side down) on a plate with a quarter cup of water. Microwave the squash for 8 to 10 minutes or until it's soft to the touch. Let it cool, then scrape out the "spaghetti" strands and top with low sugar marinara sauce and cheese.

Carbohydrates Eliminated: Squash = 30 g per cup! Zucchini = 40 g per cup!
The Taste Test: "Great. Spaghetti squash has exactly the same consistency as real pasta."

Pasta Substitutions (Per Cup)					
Item	Rating	Carbs	Sugars	Fiber	Calories
White Pasta	Bad	43	0	5	246
Rice Noodles	Bad	43	0	1.5	195
Spaghetti Squash	OK	10	4	2	42
Bean Sprouts	Best	6	4	2	31
Artichoke Hearts	Best	6	0	4	40
Cabbage Noodles	Best	5	3	2	22
Eggplant (lasagna noodles)	Best	5	2	3	20
Daikon Noodles	Best	5	0	3	25
Zucchini Noodles	Best	4	2	1	20
Miracle Noodles	Best	0	0	0	0
Kelp Noodles	Best	1	0	1	6
Shaved Deli Meat (Enchilada)	Best	0	0	0	30

HELPFUL HINT For the Kelp noodles: put them in a crock pot on low for 5-6 hours to make them soft like pasta.

BAKING Substitutes: In my family we treat corn, carrots, potatoes and rice as starchy foods, as if they were sweets (starch and sugar = excess weight gain). They are all starchy carbohydrates as are the products made from them (chips, cereal, rice cakes and snacks). So we never use alternative flours made from corn, rice or potatoes. 4 grams of carbohydrates from sugar or starch becomes 1 teaspoon of sugar in our body!

Flour Substitutions (Per Cup)					
Item	Rating	Carbs	Sugars	Fiber	Calories
Rice Flour (Gluten-Free)	Bad	127	0.2	3.8	578
White Flour	Bad	100	0	4	496
Wheat Flour	Bad	87	0	14	407
Oat Flour	Bad	78	0	12	480
Almond Flour	Best	24	4	12	640
Almond Bran	Best	40	0	38	156
Coconut Flour	Best	80	0	48	480
Flaxseed Meal	Best	32	0	32	480
Psyllium Husk	Best	80	0	72	280
Whey/Egg White Protein	Best	1	0	0	440

7 Reasons to LOVE butter from grass fed cows!

1. It is a great source of fat-soluble vitamins E, D and K. These essential nutrients are especially beneficial for children and expectant mothers. As the use of butter in America has declined, sterility rates and problems with sexual development have increased. When animals consume butter substitutes, their growth is stunted and they are unable to sustain reproduction.

2. It protects cartilage and acts as a joint lubricant. Is that fat-free diet causing joint pain?

3. It has CLA, Conjugated Linoleic Acid, which it helps build muscle and prevents weight gain. CLA also has strong cancer fighting properties. CLA disappears when cows are fed dry hay or processed feed; instead of purchasing CLA supplements, spending a few extra dollars on butter from grass-fed cows is worth it.

4. It increases the absorption of minerals such as magnesium and calcium.

5. It is rich in vitamin A, which is necessary for vision and a healthy immune system.

6. It has Glycosphingolipids. This fat may be new to most of you. It is very helpful in preventing gastrointestinal infections, particularly in children and the elderly. For this reason, young children who drink skimmed milk have diarrhea at rates up to five times greater than children who drink whole milk.

7. It tastes AMAZING!

It is a sad fact that patients are being told to use Canola and vegetable oils in place of the heathy and natural saturated fats. Vegetable oils and trans-fats are causing so much harm to our cells. These oils are also producing omega 6 in our body. Recent research has revealed that too much omega-6 in the diet creates an imbalance that can cause inflammation. This results in increased risk of blood clots, high blood pressure, and irritation of the digestive tract, depressed immune function, sterility, cancer and weight gain. Instead of being eliminated, trans fats are allowed into cells as if they were natural fats and our cells become partially hydrogenated! Once our cells become hydrogenated, our metabolism slows, not to mention the scary connection to cancer, digestive disorders and other diseases. Your body takes 9 months to rid our cells of trans-fats.

Partially hydrogenated margarines are worse for you than the extremely refined vegetable oils which they come from because of chemical processes that occur during the hydrogenation process. The extremely high temperatures, and the nickel that causes the hydrogen atoms to change position makes these items very harmful to our heart, cells and waistline! Before hydrogenation, pairs of hydrogen atoms occur together on the chain; this pattern is commonly found in nature. After hydrogenation, one hydrogen atom of the pair is moved to the other side so that the molecule straightens. This is called the trans formation, and is rarely found in nature. These factory-made trans fats are toxins to the body, but sadly our digestive system does not identify them as such. Until lately, saturated fats were usually lumped together with trans-fats in U.S. data bases that scientists use to connect dietary trends with diseases. And this is where a lot of misinformation comes in about natural saturated fats.

These man-made fats actually block use of essential fatty acids and increase omega-6 in our body. Recent research has revealed that too much omega-6 in the diet creates an imbalance that can cause inflammation. This problem can result in increased tendency to form blood clots, high blood pressure, and irritation of the digestive tract, depressed immune function, sterility, cancer and weight gain, not to mention the scary connection to cancer, digestive disorders and other diseases. Professor Walter Willett, the principal investigator at Harvard, called hydrogenation "the biggest food processing disaster in US history". In 2004 he told an interviewer that the advice to switch from butter to vegetable oils hydrogenated into margarine had turned out to be "a disastrous mistake".

1. Cholesterol, along with saturated fats, gives our cells required stiffness and stability. When the diet contains an excess of polyunsaturated fats (vegetable oils or omega-6), instead of saturated fats in the cell membrane, the cell walls become flabby. Our blood vessels become damaged in a number of ways - through irritations caused by free radicals, or because they are structurally weak. When this happens, the body's natural healing substance steps in to repair the damage, causing us to make more cholesterol. The blood drives into the tissues to give them structural integrity. This is why serum cholesterol levels may go down temporarily when we replace saturated fats with polyunsaturated fats in the diet.

2. Cholesterol is vital for production and function of serotonin receptors in the brain. Serotonin is the body's "feel-good" chemical. Low cholesterol levels have been linked to depression and aggression. Anti-depressants often don't work for patients who are on vegetarian diets.

3. Mother's milk is VERY high in cholesterol and has an important enzyme that assists the baby in using this nutrient. Babies and children need foods high in cholesterol to guarantee proper development of the brain and nervous system (BUT we also need these as adults!!!)

4. Cholesterol acts as a precursor to important hormones that help us deal with stress and protect the body against cancer and heart disease. It is also important to our sex hormones like androgen, testosterone, estrogen and progesterone. Which is why women trying to get pregnant have more success on a high saturated fat diet!

5. Cholesterol is necessary for us to use vitamin D, which is an essential fat-soluble vitamin needed for healthy bones and nervous system, insulin production, reproduction and immune system function, proper growth, mineral metabolism, and muscle tone. So why do they fortify skim milk with Vitamin D? What a waste of money!

6. Bile, which is made from cholesterol is vital for digestion and assimilation of fats in the diet.

7. Cholesterol performs as an antioxidant; which is why cholesterol levels go up with age. It protects against free radical damage that may lead to heart disease and cancer.

8. Dietary cholesterol helps maintain the health of the intestinal wall. People on low-cholesterol vegetarian diets often develop leaky gut syndrome and other intestinal disorders.

Cholesterol can become damaged by exposure to heat and oxygen. This oxidized cholesterol tends to promote damage to the arterial cells and cause buildup of plaque in the arteries. Damaged cholesterol is found in powdered milk, which is added to reduced-fat milks to give them body. That is why I NEVER suggest drinking skim milk! Damaged cholesterol is also found in powdered eggs and in meats that have been heated to high temperatures in frying and other high temperature processes. So fast food items come into play here.

Hypothyroidism can result in high cholesterol levels. When thyroid function is poor, usually due to a diet low in usable iodine, fat-soluble vitamins and high in sugar, the blood gets filled with cholesterol as a protective mechanism, providing a large amount of minerals needed to heal tissues. Hypothyroid individuals are particularly susceptible to infections, heart disease and cancer.

Did you know that cholesterol levels are a very poor predictor of future heart attacks? The risk of future heart attacks has everything to do with excess levels of insulin. This is why diabetics are known to be at a high risk of heart disease.

Dropping Your Cholesterol Levels Will NOT Lower Your Risk Of Heart Disease, Attack, Or Strokes! Dr. Lundell, an expert in cholesterol, states that people with high cholesterol live the longest! This statement seems so incredible that it takes a long time to clear one's brainwashed mind to fully understand its importance. Yet the fact that people with high cholesterol live the longest emerges clearly from many scientific papers. ~ Uffe Ravnvskov, MD, PhD

Breakfast Pizza

Ingredients:

1 c. cottage cheese
1/2 tsp baking powder
1/2 tsp salt
1 TBS oregano
7 eggs
6 oz. shredded Mozzarella cheese
3 TBS grated Parmesan cheese
1/4 c. chopped onions
1 clove garlic
3 links of Bolinski's Organic Chicken Sausage
    (spinach garlic or other), cut into small chunks

OPTIONAL:

Olives, peppers, Italian sausage, mushrooms...
NO SUGAR Marinara sauce for dipping

Directions...

Preheat oven to 350 degrees F. Combine cottage cheese, baking powder, salt and Oregano; set aside. Beat the eggs in a large mixing bowl. Slowly add the cheeses and pizza toppings (BAKE IN MUFFIN TINS for individualized pizza toppings) or pour into a greased 10" pie plate. Bake at 350 degrees F for 40 minutes, until puffy and lightly browned. A knife inserted into the center of the quiche should come out clean. Let rest for 15 minutes, top with marinara sauce and enjoy.

Makes 12 servings.
NUTRITIONAL COMPARISON (per serving)
Traditional Quiche with Crust =
290 calories, 19g fat, 10.8g protein, 19g carbs, trace fiber (19g effective carbs)
"Healthified" Quiche =
112 calories, 6.9g fat, 9.4g protein, 2.1g carbs, trace fiber (2.1g effective carbs)

Greek Quiche

Ingredients:

7 oz. feta cheese
10 oz. fresh spinach, chopped
1/4 c. onion, chopped
2 TBS of coconut oil or butter
5 eggs
1 clove garlic, minced

PIE CRUST:
3 c. blanched almond flour
1/2 tsp Celtic sea salt
4 TBS of butter, cold and cut into small pieces
1 egg
1 clove garlic, crushed

Directions...

Preheat oven to 325 degrees F. In a medium sized bowl, mix together almond flour, salt, butter, garlic and egg. Press pie crust into pie dish or tart pan. Bake the crust for 12-15 minutes, or until it starts to lightly brown.

Sauté the chopped spinach and onions in oil until the onions are translucent. Turn the heat off and add the cheese and eggs to the spinach; mix until well combined. Pour the spinach filling into the pie crust and bake for 15-20 minutes, or until the filling is set and the eggs are fully cooked through.

Makes 12 servings.
Nutritional Comparison (per serving):

Traditional Quiche =
334 calories, 12g fat, 9g protein, 27g carbs, 1.5g fiber (25.5g effective carbs)
"Healthified" Quiche =
301 calories, 24g fat, 11.9g protein, 8g carbs, 3.6g fiber (4.4g effective carbs)

In my book, Secrets to Controlling Your Weight Cravings and Mood, I discuss the main neurotransmitters responsible for a healthy brain (serotonin, GABA, dopamine and acetylcholine). Most people haven't heard of acetylcholine, but it is so important! Acetylcholine controls the brain's speed and mental process, keeping memory sharp and physical movements quick and precise. Acetylcholine controls activity in the parietal lobe, the area of the brain responsible for processing sensory information, learning, memory and awareness. Inadequate levels of this chemical can cause characteristics like forgetfulness, difficulty prioritizing tasks and an inability to relate to others.

For most women who are predisposed to an acetylcholine deficiency, these symptoms set in with peri-menopause. Estrogen and testosterone stimulate the production of acetylcholine. As levels of those hormones decline, so does the production of this brain chemical. This prompts symptoms like memory lapses, dry skin and weight gain. The cholesterol in yolks help produce healthy hormones levels that enhance our skin, mood, sex drive as well as many other important roles. The reason why cholesterol levels go up after menopause is because your body is trying to produce more estrogen (which your ovaries are no longer releasing).

Acetylcholine deficiency can spur Alzheimer's, Multiple Sclerosis, dementia, dry mouth, dry skin, reading or writing disorders, speech problems, slow movement, mood swings, learning disorders, verbal memory problems, memory lapses, attention problems, difficulty concentrating, carelessness, and decreased creativity. If you crave fatty foods or have perfectionist tendencies you may also benefit from more acetylcholine. When acetylcholine deficits are corrected, most experience increased mental clarity, greater creativity, quicker thinking and improved empathy.

In the late 1930s, scientists discovered that tissue from the pancreas contained a substance called Choline, which helps prevent fatty build-up in the liver and produces acetylcholine. Since then, research has shown that choline is found not only in the pancreas and liver, but is also a huge component of every human cell.

Choline is named after the Greek word which means bile, which is very appropriate. Bile, which is produced in our liver, has a primary job of making fat compatible with water, so that fat-based matter can get transported though the body in our water-based blood. Interestingly, Choline has very comparable fat-modifying effects on our cellular membrane. The reason that choline decreases fat storage is that it allows our cell membranes to operate with greater flexibility in handling both fat and water-soluble molecules. In other words, without choline, fat-based nutrients and waste products could not pass in and out of our cells. Therefore, healthy fats can't get into our cells to make our brain healthy, skin soft, and cells happy AND we can't get the stored toxic fat out!

Choline is a key component of the fat-containing structures in cell membranes. Since cell membranes are almost entirely made up of fats, the membranes' health depends on adequate amounts of choline. In the brain, these fat-like molecules are responsible for a very high percentage of total solids, so choline is predominantly important for brain health, and its use in brain disorders is immense.

To produce more acetylcholine, enjoy three servings of choline-rich foods; like eggs (I'm talking about the yolks here…Egg Beaters don't count). Grass-fed, organic eggs are the most beneficial. Grass-fed eggs contain a very high level of healthy omega-3s compared to store-bought eggs. Omega 3 will also stimulate a happier brain by assisting our cells to communicate. "Happy cells are talking cells." Supplemental choline has even shown effectiveness in treating Alzheimer's disease.

In addition to poor dietary intake of choline itself, poor intake of other nutrients, like B-vitamins and amino acids, can result in a choline deficiency. Liver problems, including cirrhosis, are common contributing factors to choline deficiency. Certain procedures, such as by-pass surgery and kidney transplants are also direct causes of a choline deficiency.

So try this recipe filled with yolk-rich choline!

Waffles Eggs Benedict on an English Muffin. Use Toasted Sub bread for English Muffin shapes.

Waffle Eggs Benedict

Ingredients:

1 c. almond flour
    or (1/2 c. coconut flour)
1 c. vanilla egg white
    or whey protein (Jay Robb)
1/2 tsp Celtic sea salt
1 TBS aluminum free baking powder
1 c. unsweetened almond milk
    (1 1/2 if using coconut flour)
2 eggs (4 eggs if using coconut flour)
4 TBS butter or coconut oil, melted

HOLLANDAISE:
6 large egg yolks
1/4 c. lemon juice
2 TBS Dijon mustard
1 1/2 c. melted unsalted butter
1/2 tsp Celtic sea salt
1/8 tsp freshly ground black pepper
1/8 tsp cayenne

TOPPINGS
12 prosciutto or ham slices
12 eggs

Directions...

Preheat waffle iron to high (make sure it is Hot Hot Hot or the waffles will stick). Combine the dry ingredients in a bowl. Combine the wet ingredients in another bowl. Slowly add the wet ingredients into the dry. Let sit for 5 minutes. Bake according to your waffle iron directions. Set aside.

MAKE HOLLANDAISE SAUCE: In the bottom of a double boiler or in a medium saucepan, bring 1 inch of water to a simmer over high heat and adjust heat to maintain simmer. Put egg yolks, lemon juice, and mustard in top of a double boiler or in a round-bottomed medium bowl and set over simmering water. Whisk yolk mixture to blend. Whisking constantly, add butter in a slow, steady stream (it should take about 90 seconds). Cook sauce, whisking, until it reaches 140°, then adjust heat to maintain temperature (remove from simmering water if necessary). Add salt, pepper, and cayenne and continue whisking until thick, about 3 minutes. Adjust seasonings to taste. Remove from stove and set aside. This will make extra. Poach eggs: Bring 1 in. water to boil in a 12-in.-wide pan. Lower heat so that small bubbles form on the bottom of the pan and break to the surface only occasionally. Crack eggs into water 1 at a time, holding shells close to the water's surface and letting eggs slide out gently. Poach eggs in 2 batches to keep them from crowding, 3 to 4 minutes for soft-cooked. Lift eggs out with a slotted spoon, pat dry with a paper towel.

Place a waffle onto a plate, top with a few slices of prosciutto or ham, 2 poached eggs and drizzle with 2 TBS hollandaise sauce.

Makes 6 servings.
NUTRITIONAL COMPARISON (per serving)
Traditional Eggs Benedict =
424 calories, 27g fat, 15g protein, 33g carbs, 1g fiber (32g effective carbs)
"Healthified" Eggs Benedict =
373 calories, 29g fat, 21.5g protein, 5.3g carbs, 1.4g fiber (3.9g effective carbs)

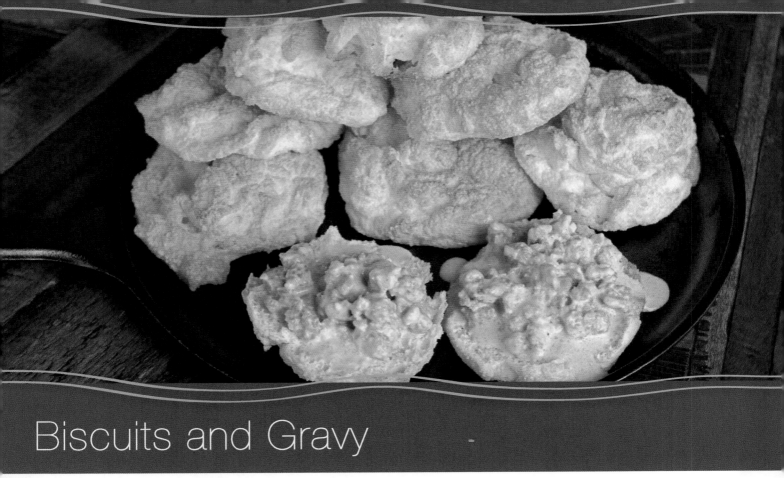

Biscuits and Gravy

Ingredients:

4 egg whites
1 c. almond flour
1 tsp baking powder
2 TBS chilled butter (cut into pieces)
1/4 tsp Celtic sea salt
OPTIONS: add 1 tsp of garlic or
your favorite spice

GRAVY:
10 oz. Organic Prairie
    pork sausage, crumbled
1 c. cream cheese
1 c. organic beef or chicken broth
Celtic sea salt and ground
    black pepper to taste

Directions...

BISCUITS: Preheat oven to 400 degrees F. Grease a cookie sheet (or muffin tin) with coconut oil spray. Whip egg whites until very fluffy. In a separate medium bowl, mix the baking powder into the almond flour. Then cut in the butter and salt (if the butter isn't chilled, the biscuits won't be fluffy, crispy and buttery) Gently fold in the dry mixture into the whites. Dollop the dough onto the cookie sheet (or muffin tin) and bake for 11-15 minutes.

Makes 8 servings.
NUTRITIONAL COMPARISON:
KFC Biscuit = 220 calories, 24 carbs, 1g fiber
"Healthified" Biscuit = 113 calories, 3 carbs, 1.5 fiber

GRAVY: Cook sausage in large skillet over medium heat 5-6 minutes or until thoroughly heated, stirring frequently. Gradually add cream cheese and broth; cook until mixture comes to a soft simmer and thickens, stirring constantly until smooth. Reduce heat to medium-low; simmer 2 minutes, stirring constantly. Season to taste with salt and pepper. Split biscuits in half. Place 2 halves on each of 8 plates; top with about 1/3 cup gravy.

Makes 8 servings.
NUTRITIONAL COMPARISON (per serving)

Traditional Biscuits and Gravy =
353 calories, 19g fat, 9.8g protein, 31g carbs, 0.5g fiber (30.5g effective carbs)

"Healthified" Biscuits and Gravy =
345 calories, 29.9g fat, 14.6g protein, 4.9g carbs, 1.5g fiber (3.4g effective carbs)

Cheezy Bacon Scones

Ingredients:

2 c. blanched almond flour
1 tsp Celtic sea salt
1 TBS baking powder
4 TBS cold butter
1 c. (4 oz.) diced cheddar cheese OR crumbled blue cheese
1/3 c. chopped fresh chives
1/2 lb (1 c. cooked and crumbled) bacon
3/4 c. unsweetened almond milk

Directions... Preheat the oven to 375 degrees F. Lightly grease a baking sheet, or line it with parchment. In a medium bowl, stir together the almond flour, salt, and baking powder. Cut the butter into the flour until the mixture is unevenly crumbly, with some of the butter remaining in larger pieces. Mix in the cheese, chives, and bacon until evenly distributed. Add the almond milk stirring to combine. Try squeezing the dough together; if it's crumbly and won't hang together, or if there are crumbs remaining in the bottom of the bowl, add 2 more TBS of almond milk until the dough comes together. Transfer the dough to a piece of greased parchment paper. Pat the dough into a smooth 7" disk about ¾" thick. Transfer to a prepared baking sheet. Use a knife or bench knife to cut the disk into 12 wedges, spreading the wedges apart a bit on the pan. Bake the scones for 22 to 24 minutes, until they're golden brown. Remove them from the oven, and cool right on the pan. Serve warm, or at room temperature.

Makes 12 scones.
NUTRITIONAL COMPARISON (per serving)
Traditional Scone = 294 calories, 18g fat, 10g protein, 18g carbs, 0.6g fiber (17.4g effective carbs)
"Healthified" Scone = 292 calories, 24g fat, 13.6g protein, 5.3g carbs, 2.1g fiber (3.2g effective carbs)

Pinwheel Crackers

Ingredients:

1/4 c. butter, softened at room temperature
8 oz. crumbled blue cheese
1 1/2 c. blanched almond flour
1/2 c. finely chopped walnuts
Pinch of Celtic sea salt (optional)

Directions... In a large mixing bowl, use a mixer to beat butter and cheese until smooth. Add almond flour, and salt and mix until well-combined. Dump the dough onto a piece of parchment or a greased piece of plastic wrap, press it into a ball, and roll into a 12-inch long log. Brush the log completely with the egg wash. Spread the walnuts in a square on a cutting board and roll the log back and forth in the walnuts, pressing lightly, and distributing them evenly on the outside of the log. Wrap in plastic and refrigerate for at least 30 minutes or for up to 4 days Meanwhile, preheat the oven to 350 degrees F.

Cut the log 3/8ths-inch thick with a small, sharp knife and place the crackers on a sheet pan lined with parchment paper. Bake for 22 minutes until very lightly browned. Rotate the pan once during baking. Cool and serve at room temperature.

Makes 18 servings (36 crackers).
NUTRITIONAL COMPARISON (per serving):
Traditional Nut Thins = 130 Calories, 2.5g fat, 3g protein, 23g carb, trace fiber (23g effective carbs)
"Healthified" Nut Crackers = 145 calories, 12g fat, 6g protein, 2.6g carb, 1.2g fiber (1.2g effective carbs)

Crohn's and Colitis

I see many clients with a variety of problems. One issue on the rise is Crohn's and Colitis. If Crohn's disease and ulcerative colitis are caught before serious damage has been done, both conditions can be treated simply by restricting carbohydrates. Carbohydrates, sugar and vegetable oils are extremely inflammatory and terrible for our intestinal health. Could the increase in carbohydrates and sugar be the cause of all these problems? In 1840 the average person consumed 2 tsp of sugar a day and in 2009 a typical person consumed over 63 tsp every day!

The main thing to avoid is long chained triglycerides. Long-chain triglyceride impairs the healing time in active Crohn's disease. These fatty acids are substrates for inflammatory eicosanoid production. Red meat has long been wrongly blamed for IBS. A study published in December 2009 shows that linoleic acid harms intestinal health but news reports and health websites mislead by blaming 'red meat' — which contains the least linoleic acid. It's the polyunsaturated fats and oils, derived from seeds such as sunflower, safflower, soy and corn, which are the major dietary sources of linoleic acid; they are the most harmful oils for those with intestinal problems because they increase inflammation.

When it is absorbed in the intestinal lining, linoleic acid is transformed to arachidonic acid, which is a component of the cell membranes in the bowel. Arachidonic acid can then be converted into various inflammatory chemicals. High levels of these chemicals have been found in the intestinal tissue of people suffering from intestinal disorders.

Long chained triglycerides come from VEGETABLE OILS...this means anything that is pre-packaged; salad dressings, roasted nuts, "baked" chips, popcorn, crackers, cereal...you name it! We have been wrongly pushed to replace healthy saturated fats like coconut oil with harmful fats such as canola!

Coconut oil is a medium-chained fatty acid. MCFA are broken down almost immediately by enzymes in the saliva and gastric juices so that pancreatic fat-digesting enzymes are not even essential. Therefore, there is less strain on the pancreas and digestive system. People with the highest intake of omega-3 fatty acid also known as docosahexanoic acid reduced the complications of Crohn's and colitis by 77%. omega-3 fatty acid is found in oily fish such as salmon and sardines. They are called "essential" Omega 3 because your body can't make them, therefore, you must consume omegas through food. When we replace harmful vegetable oils with healthy omega-3s, there is less strain on the pancreas and digestive system. This has important implications for patients who suffer from digestive and metabolic problems. Since it is easily absorbed in the digestive tract it also helps other essential healing nutrients become absorbed as well. Ulcerative colitis often begins with a virus or a bacterial infection and that the body's immune system malfunctions and stays active after the infection has cleared. Coconut has antimicrobial properties that affects intestinal health by killing troublesome microorganisms that may cause chronic inflammation. Coconut oil resembles breast milk more than any other food...breast milk helps keep babies healthy!

Cornbread made in a cast iron skillet.
Are you a female, an athlete, or have a food allergy and are low in iron? Iron is very important to especially if you are female (about 90% of females are iron deficient and this is why they don't have enough energy and are losing hair). If you lack iron you have a hard time carrying oxygen to the mitochondria of you cell, which is where you burn fat. SO, if you are low in iron, fat burning is hard to accomplish. Low iron can be caused by a FOOD SENSITIVITY (your intestines inhibit you from absorbing iron), heavy menstrual cycles, heavy exercising, or not eating meat. Low iron causes high anxiety. Cooking in a cast iron skillet helps increase iron in your cells.

"Corn" Bread

Ingredients:

1/2 c. coconut flour
1/4 tsp Celtic sea salt
1/4 tsp baking soda
6 eggs
1/2 c. coconut oil, melted OR
  unsweetened almond milk

OPTIONS:

CINNAMON SWIRL:
add in 1 TBS cinnamon

ROSEMARY BREAD:
1 TBS fresh rosemary
Or other herbs of your choice

Directions...
Preheat oven to 350 degrees F. In a medium sized bowl sift together the dry ingredients. Slowly add the wet ingredients into the dry ingredients and stir until very smooth. Grease a cake pan (or muffin tin) and fill about 2/3 of the way full with batter. Bake for 40-50 minutes, or until a toothpick comes out clean.

Makes 12 servings.
NUTRITIONAL COMPARISON (per serving)

Traditional Bread =
82 calories, 1g fat, 1g protein, 21g carbs, trace fiber (21g effective carbs)

"Healthified" Bread (oil) =
132 calories, 11g fat, 3.4g protein, 2.8g carbs, 1.7g fiber (1.1g effective carbs)

"Healthified" Bread (almond milk) =
54 calories, 2.8g fat, 3.5g protein, 2.9g carbs, 1.7g fiber (1.2g effective carbs)

*Enjoy this bread with a big bowl of organic bone broth if you are suffering from illness.

Tortillas

Ingredients:

1 1/4 c. blanched almond flour
 (or 1/2 c. coconut flour)
5 TBS psyllium husk powder
1 tsp Celtic sea salt
2 TBS butter
2 eggs (4 if using coconut flour)
1 c. hot water
 (or marinara - for Tomato Basil wrap)

Directions...
In a medium sized bowl, combine the almond/coconut flour, psyllium powder (no substitutes: flaxseed meal won't work), and salt. Add in the eggs and combine until a thick dough. Boil the water (or marinara) and add into the bowl. Mix until well combined. Let sit for a minute or two until the dough gels up. Separate into 10 balls (about 2 inches in diameter). Place the dough onto a piece of greased parchment paper. Top with another greased piece of parchment. Using a rolling pin, roll the dough out in a circle shape with even thickness throughout. This dough is very forgiving, so if you don't make a circle with the rolling pin, use your hands to perfect your tortilla. Heat a large pan to medium-high heat with coconut oil or coconut oil spray. Once hot, place an unbaked tortilla on the pan (if the tortilla sticks to the parchment the first time, as it did for me, use your hands to close up any holes...the dough is still very forgiving) and sauté until light brown, then flip and bake through.

Makes 10 servings. NUTRITIONAL COMPARISON (per tortilla)
Traditional Tortilla = 140 calories, 3g fat, 4g protein, 25g carbs, trace fiber (25g effective carbs)
Almond Flour Tortilla = 105 calories, 7.5g fat, 4.1g protein, 5.6g carb, 3.8g fiber (1.8g effective carbs)
Coconut Flour Tortilla = 71 calories, 2.6g fat, 3.4g protein, 7.4g carbs, 5.2g fiber (2.2g effective carbs)

Protein Popovers

Ingredients:

1 c. Jay Robb unflavored whey protein (or vanilla for a sweet popover)
2 c. unflavored almond milk
4 eggs
1/2 tsp Celtic sea salt
4 TBS coconut oil OR butter, melted (plus extra for greasing)

Directions...
Preheat the oven to 425 degree F. Grease popover tins with butter or coconut oil spray. Place the tins in the hot oven for about 8 minutes. Meanwhile, in a medium sized bowl blend together the whey, almond milk, eggs and salt.

Carefully remove hot tin from oven. Dollop 1 tsp of butter or coconut oil into each hot cup and pour the batter in until 2/3 full. Bake for 15 minutes at 425 degree F. Leave the oven closed and reduce heat to 325 degree F to bake for an additional 10-12 minutes.

I love mine topped with a little butter and Nature's Hollow Xylitol Honey! But the family loves them served with dinner!

Makes 12 servings. NUTRITIONAL COMPARISON (per popover)
Traditional Popover = 152 calories, 7g fat, 2g protein, 20g carbs, 0g fiber (20g effective carbs)
"Healthified" Popover = 106 calories, 7g fat, 10g protein, 1.2g carbs, 0g fiber (1.2g effective carbs)

Ingredients:

1/2 c. coconut flour
2 TBS psyllium husk powder
1/4 tsp Celtic sea salt
1/4 c. butter OR
    coconut oil, softened
1 c. boiling veggie broth OR
    water (broth adds flavor)

OPTIONAL FLAVOR ADDITIONS:
1/4 tsp garlic powder
1/2 tsp oregano

Directions...

Preheat the oven to 350 degrees F. In a medium sized bowl, stir together the coconut flour, psyllium husks, salt and any spices you desire. Add the butter or coconut oil. Stir continuously as you add the hot broth or water, it will melt the butter or oil. Combine until very smooth.

Separate into 3 rolls. Place one roll of dough onto a piece of greased parchment paper. Top the dough with another piece of greased parchment. Using a rolling pin, roll the dough out in a circle shape with even thickness throughout. Remove the top parchment. Place the bottom parchment with the unbaked wraps onto a cookie sheet. Bake at 350 degrees F for 20 minutes or until done throughout (this will depend on how thick you rolled the dough). Use for sandwiches!

NOTE: Bake the dough right away; it starts to cook once you add in the broth/water.

Makes 3 wraps.
NUTRITIONAL COMPARISON (per 1/2 wrap)

Traditional Wrap =
180 calories, 5g fat, 2g protein, 30g carbs, 3g fiber (27g effective carbs)
"Healthified" Wrap =
123 calories, 8.7g fat, 2g protein, 9.3g carbs, 6.7g fiber (2.6g effective carbs)

* Some psyllium powder will turn your baked goods a dark "rye bread" color.
To avoid this problem, I grind Jay Robb psyllium husks into a fine powder.

Try any of the endless possibilities. The Chicken Club Sub is pictured above and the Meatball Sub is pictured below.

Toasted Sub

Ingredients:

1 1/4 c. blanched almond flour
    (or 1/2 cup coconut flour)
5 TBS psyllium husk powder
    (no substitutes)
2 tsp baking powder
1 tsp Celtic sea salt
2 egg whites (8 egg whites if
    using coconut flour)
1 c. boiling water
    (or MARINARA - for more
    Tomato Basil Bread!)

Directions...

Preheat the oven to 350 degrees F. In a medium sized bowl, combine the flour, psyllium powder (no substitutes: flaxseed meal won't work), baking powder and salt. Add in the eggs and combine until a thick dough. Add boiling water or marinara into the bowl. Mix until well combined. Form into 4 to 5 mini subs (the dough will rise and spread) or one large sub/loaf and place onto a greased baking sheet. Bake for 65 minutes. Remove from the oven and allow the bread cool completely. Cut open with a serrated knife. Stuff with desired fillings. OPTION: Double the batch and bake in a small bread pan to make a PANINI!

Makes 5 servings.
NUTRITIONAL COMPARISON (per serving)
Traditional Sub Bread = 180 calories, 6g fat, 4g protein, 41g carbs, trace fiber (41g effective carbs)
Almond Flour Sub = 180 calories, 12g fat, 7.3g protein, 10.8g carb, 7.6g fiber (3.2g effective carbs)
Coconut Flour Bread = 137 calories, 1.1g fat, 14.7g protein, 15g carbs, 10.4g fiber (4.6g effective carbs)

FILLING IDEAS:

CHICKEN CLUB: Smoked Chicken, bacon, tomatoes, lettuce, onions

TUNA MELT: Tuna, tomato, sharp cheddar: toast in a broiler until bread is crispy and cheese is melted

MEATBALL SUB: use my "healthified" meatballs and no sugar marinara

PIZZA SUB: fill with your favorite pizza toppings, no sugar marinara, mozzarella: toast in a broiler until bread is crispy and cheese is melted

VARIATIONS:

"EVERYTHING" Bagel:
add 1/2 tsp dill
1/2 tsp dried chives
1/2 tsp dried parsley
1/2 tsp onion powder
1/4 tsp garlic
2 TBS parmesan cheese

ONION Bagel:
add 1 tsp dried onion flakes

CINNAMON Bagel:
add 2 tsp cinnamon
1 tsp stevia glycerite and
1 tsp vanilla
(and use vanilla whey
instead of unflavored)

Bagels

Ingredients:

5 eggs
1/4 c. coconut oil or butter, melted
½ tsp Celtic sea salt
1/4 c. coconut flour
1/4 c. unflavored whey protein
1 tsp aluminum free baking powder

OPTIONAL:
1 tsp guar gum or xanthan gum
(for a chewy texture)

Directions...
Preheat the oven to 375 degrees F. Blend together eggs, coconut oil/butter, salt, and spices if using. In a separate bowl, mix coconut flour and whey with baking powder and guar gum. Blend the dry mixture into the wet until smooth. Grease a donut pan with coconut oil spray. Pour dough into pan. Bake for 15 minutes.

Makes 6 bagels.
NUTRITIONAL COMPARISON (per bagel)
Lender's New York Bagel =
270 calories, 4g fat, 6g protein, 55g carbs, 8g fiber (47g effective carbs)
"Healthified" Bagel =
161 calories, 13g fat, 8g protein, 2.9g carbs, 1.7g fiber (1.2g effective carbs)

Cinnamon FUN HERB FACT

1/2 teaspoon of cinnamon per day can lower your bad cholesterol (or LDL). Cinnamon lowers blood sugar levels. Its antifungal properties, can kills candida. Cinnamon reduces leukemia and lymphoma cancer cells. Cinnamon has an anti-clotting effect on the blood. Cinnamon has been found to relieve arthritis pain. When added to food, cinnamon inhibits bacterial growth and food spoilage, making it a natural food preservative. Just smelling cinnamon boosts cognitive function and memory. Cinnamon fights the E. coli bacteria in unpasteurized juices. Cinnamon has been found to be an effective natural remedy for eliminating headaches and migraine relief. Cinnamon can also help stabilize blood sugar (which is great for weight loss). A couple of dashes in your morning tea is all it takes!

Coconut
Curry

Tomato
Basil

Cilantro Lime

GRISSINI (Italian Bread Sticks)

Ingredients:

BASE RECIPE:
1 c. blanched almond flour
1 TBS coconut flour
1 TBS Jay Robb unflavored whey protein powder
1 tsp baking powder
1/2 tsp Celtic sea salt

FLAVOR IDEAS:

TOMATO BASIL:
Add 4 TBS marinara sauce, 4 TBS fresh chopped basil

CILANTRO LIME:
Add 4 TBS lime juice, 1/4 cup fresh chopped cilantro

COCONUT CURRY:
Add 4 TBS coconut milk, 1 1/2 TBS green curry paste

Directions...
Preheat the oven to 300 degrees F. In a medium sized bowl, mix the base ingredients until well mixed. Add in your favorite flavor ingredients. Mix until the dough is very dense and a tiny bit sticky. Wet your hands and roll out into long bread stick shapes. Place the sticks on a greased piece of parchment and place on a cookie sheet or place the sticks right onto a pizza stone (using a pizza stone helps to absorb moisture and makes the bread-sticks nice and crisp). Bake for 20 minutes or until light golden. Turn oven off and keep them in the oven for another 10 minutes to crisp up.

Makes 8 servings.
NUTRITIONAL COMPARISON (per serving)
Traditional Breadstick =
130 calories, 4g fat, 4g protein, 20g carbs, 1g fiber (19g effective carbs)
"Healthified" Breadstick =
97 calories, 7g fat, 4g protein, 4.7g carbs, 2g fiber (2.7g effective carbs)

Pesto and Olive Rolls

Directions...

TO MAKE: Use Toasted Sub dough recipe, grease a large piece of parchment with coconut oil spray and roll the dough out into a large rectangle. Spread pesto or olive tapenade all over the dough. Starting at one edge of the rectangle, roll up tightly until you have a cylinder. Cut into 12 - 2 inch rolls. Place onto a cookie sheet and bake for 25-30 minutes or until golden brown.

NOTE: Nutritional information is based off of bread only.

Makes 5 servings.
NUTRITIONAL COMPARISON (per serving)
Traditional Rolls = 180 calories, 6g fat, 4g protein, 41g carbs, trace fiber (41g effective carbs)
Almond Flour Rolls = 205 calories, 14g fat, 8.4g protein, 10.9g carb, 7.6g fiber (3.3 effective carbs)
Coconut Flour Rolls = 142 calories, 5g fat, 6.8g protein, 14.8g carbs, 10.4g fiber (4.4 effective carbs)

Agave and Fructose

Have you looked at the ingredients in your BBQ sauce? The first ingredient is usually corn syrup, NOT tomatoes! But maybe you are saying, "I make my own already." But how are you making it? My mom still uses ketchup...and what is ketchup? Nothing but gooey-red corn syrup. You may be thinking, "Well, I don't buy the ketchup with high fructose corn syrup, I get the agave-sweetened brands at health food stores," but that is no better. Agave syrup is marketed as "low glycemic" and that is true, but let's look into why agave syrup is "low glycemic." It is due to the shockingly high concentration of fructose. It is 90% fructose and 10% glucose. Sugar is about 50/50% fructose to glucose, honey is about 55% fructose, high fructose corn syrup can range from 55-65% fructose.

Why FRUCTOSE is so harmful:

1. Fructose can only be metabolized by the liver and it raises triglycerides (blood fats) like no other food. Fructose bypasses the enzyme phosphofructokinase, which is the rate-limiting enzyme for glucose metabolism. Fructose is shunted past the sugar-regulating pathways and into the fat-formation pathway. The liver converts this fructose to fat, which, unfortunately, remains in the liver causing FATTY LIVER DISEASE. Consuming fructose is essentially consuming fat! This is why I see so many children with fatty liver disease...they aren't drinking alcohol, they are drinking sodas, juices and consuming too much fructose!

2. Fructose reduces the sensitivity of insulin receptors, which causes type II diabetes. Insulin receptors are the way glucose enters a cell to be metabolized. Our cells become resistant to the effects of insulin and as a result, the body needs to make more insulin to handle the same amount of glucose. We also start to produce insulin as a defense mechanism even if we don't eat sugar or starch. YIKES! This is why we shouldn't allow our children to eat so much sugar and starch either...even though they are thin and active, you are setting them up for an adulthood where they can't enjoy a dessert without reaping the adverse effects. I grew up on Fruity Pebbles and skim milk for breakfast, and Cocoa Pebbles for dinner, which is why I am so sensitive to glucose.

3. Fructose is high in uric acid, which increases blood pressure and causes gout.

4. Fructose increases lactic acid in the blood. High levels cause metabolic acidosis especially for those with conditions such as diabetes.

5. Fructose changes the collagen of our skin making it prone to wrinkles and oxidative damage.

6. High consumption of fructose leads to mineral losses: iron, calcium magnesium and zinc, which leads to low bone density (osteoporosis). It also interferes with copper metabolism. This causes collagen and elastin being unable to form, which are connective tissue that hold the body together. A deficiency in copper can also lead to infertility, bone loss, anemia, or defective arteries, infertility, high cholesterol levels, heart attacks and inability to control blood sugar.

7. Fructose has no effect on our hunger hormone ghrelin and interferes with brain's communication with leptin, which is the hormone that tells us to stop eating and you CAN become leptin resistant!

Carolina BBQ Sauce

Ingredients:

1 c. yellow mustard
¼ c. Nature's Hollow xylitol honey (or Swerve)
¾ c. cider or coconut vinegar
1 TBS chili powder
1 tsp ground black pepper
1 tsp ground white pepper
¼ tsp cayenne pepper
½ tsp Organic Tamari sauce (soy sauce)
2 TBS butter or coconut oil, melted
1 tsp liquid smoke flavoring

Directions...

In a saucepan over medium heat, stir together the mustard, sweetener, cider vinegar, chili powder, black pepper, white pepper, and cayenne pepper. Simmer for 30 minutes. Stir in the Tamari sauce, butter, and liquid smoke; simmer for 10 more minutes. Cool completely, and refrigerate overnight to blend flavors before using.

Makes 16 servings.
NUTRITIONAL COMPARISON (per serving)
Traditional BBQ sauce =
71 calories, 0g fat, 0g protein, 15g carbs, trace fiber (15g effective carbs)
"Healthified" BBQ sauce =
37 calories, 2.7g fat, 1g protein, 1.9g carbs, 1g fiber (0.9g effective carbs)

NEW INGREDIENT:

Xylitol Honey....The honey bear is the only animal found in nature with a problem with tooth-decay (honey decays teeth faster than table sugar). Honey = highest calorie content of all sugars with 65 calories/TBS, compared to the 48 calories/TBS found in table sugar.

Cayenne
FUN HERB FACT

Cayenne is a highly effective pain reliever and is an ingredient in some over-the-counter pain relieving creams. It is also great for improving circulation, healing sore throats, and stimulating sweating to help relieve cold symptoms.

MSG is used to
fatten mice so
scientists can
research obesity.
MSG is an
excito-toxin that
causes your brain
neurotransmitters
to malfunction and
causes you to eat
uncontrollably.
It is in 80 percent
of pre-packages
food and is often
disguised as
"natural flavoring."

Vitamin D Facts

Are you using fat-free salad dressing? Well, did you know that vitamins A, D, E and K are FAT-SOLUBLE vitamins? You can't absorb these vitamins without a fat, which is why fortifying skim milk with vitamin D is a waste of money! I have so many clients deficient in vitamin D. Could our low fat diets be the problem? Taking a vitamin D supplement with a bowl of cereal and skim milk will NOT let the vitamin D absorb into the bloodstream.

Having low vitamin D levels can affect us in so many ways.

1. It is a major factor for the development of type one diabetes in children.

2. Activated vitamin D in the adrenal gland regulates tyrosine hydroxylase, the rate-limiting enzyme essential for the production of dopamine, epinephrine and norepinephrine. Check out the book "Secrets to Your Weight Cravings and Mood" for more information.

3. Low vitamin D contributes to chronic fatigue and depression.

4. Insulin resistance is one of the major factors not only leading to cancer, but also to the number one killer in the US, heart disease. Northern countries have higher levels of heart disease and more heart attacks that occur in the winter months (when our vitamin D levels plummet).

5. Infertility is associated with low vitamin D.

6. PMS has been completely reversed by addition of magnesium and vitamin D.

7. Progression of degenerative arthritis is faster in people with lower vitamin D levels.

8. Autoimmune Disorders: Multiple Sclerosis, rheumatoid arthritis, thyroiditis and Crohn's disease have all been linked with low vitamin D levels.

9. Obesity: Vitamin D has recently been shown to lower leptin secretion. Leptin is a hormone produced by fat cells and is involved in weight regulation. It is a hormone signals the brain when fat cells are "full" and to stop eating.

Dill
FUN HERB FACT

Dill contains calcium and iron, and the oils in the plant may help to neutralize carcinogens, which are substances that have been shown to cause cancer. 1.5 tablespoons of dill has more calcium than a cup of whole milk. Dill also has a number of beneficial healing properties for the digestive system and has been used since ancient times to treat heartburn and also diarrhea.

Ranch Dressing

Ingredients:

1 (8 oz.) package cream cheese, softened
1/2 c. chicken or beef broth
1/2 tsp dried chives
1/2 tsp dried parsley
1/2 tsp dried dill weed
1/4 tsp garlic powder
1/4 tsp onion powder
1/8 tsp Celtic salt
1/8 tsp ground black pepper

Directions...

I know my recipe sounds a little crazy, but it tastes awesome. The cream cheese makes it so thick. This added an amazing flavor without extra calories, 1 TBS of mayo is 100 calories, 1 TBS of cream cheese is 50 calories. Since cream cheese is so much thicker, you can add a flavorful broth to thin the dressing and you save a lot of calories.

In a blender or a large bowl, mix together all the ingredients until smooth. Cover and refrigerate for 2 hours before serving (it will thicken up as it rests).

Makes 12 servings.
NUTRITIONAL COMPARISON (per serving)

Traditional Ranch =
153 calories, 15.6g fat, 0.4g protein, 1.1g carbs, 0g fiber (1.1g effective carbs)

KRAFT Fat Free Ranch =
48 calories, 0.3g fat, 0.2g protein, 11g carbs, 0g fiber (11g effective carbs)

"Healthified" Ranch =
66 calories, 5.8g fat, 2.7g protein, 0.75g carbs, 0g fiber (0.75g effective carbs)

Macadamia vs Olive Oil

My new favorite oil is macadamia nut oil! This oil has a high smoke point of around 425 degrees F. This is much higher than that of olive oil. I never fry in olive oil, I only use macadamia or coconut oil; they don't break down into products that are unhealthy for the heart. Due to its chemical structure and high amount of unsaturated fats, heating olive oil = oxidative damage. Are you leaving your bottle of olive oil right on the counter? Opening and closing it multiple times a week? Any time the olive oil is exposed to air and/or light, it oxidizes. The chlorophyll in olive oil accelerates the oxidation. Oxidation causes free radicals, which increase cancer and atherosclerosis; which are "free radical" diseases. Cancer is associated with chromosomal defects and oncogene activation. The consumption of oxidized oils increases death rates from leukemia and malignant neoplasia of the breast, ovaries and rectum. Atherosclerosis increases as free radical reactions from diet-derived fats in the arterial wall increases. These compounds induce endothelial cell damage and produce changes in the arterial walls.

WORST OILS: Canola, Corn, Cottonseed, Soy, Sunflower
FOUND IN: Microwave dinners, salad dressings, chips, cookies, crackers, roasted nuts…

On the other hand, macadamia nut oil has a long shelf life. It can be stored for up to 1 to 2 years without refrigeration. Macadamia nut oil has linoleic acid, omega-3 essential fatty acid, omega-6 fatty acid and also palmitoleic acid. The oleic acid in macadamia nut oil has anti-inflammatory properties that makes it effective in fighting against chronic diseases, such as heart disease.

Macadamia nut oil is a stable oil that is also great for topical use for all skin types. I love macadamia oil for use on dry and mature skin due to its high concentration of palmitoleic acid. This acid is naturally present in human sebum when we are young and declines as we age; it softens and moisturizes the skin and also helps in healing mild wounds. Macadamia oil is absorbed very easily by the skin and the scalp and helps the cells to rejuvenate. It prevents sunburns and also helps the skin retain its moisture.

It also acts as an antioxidant. It prevents damage to skin cells by free radicals that cause signs of aging on the skin. Macadamia nut oil skin care is also attributed to its high vitamin E content. Macadamia oil is also a rich source of calcium, vitamin B complex and minerals like phosphorus and iron. Macadamia nut oil is very tasty for salads; it has a natural "nutty" flavor.

Caprese salad

drizzled with

Super Salad

Dressing.

See page 31.

Super Salad Dressing

Ingredients:

1/2 c. macadamia nut oil
4 TBS white vinegar or coconut vinegar
1/2 tsp stevia glycerite
1 tsp Celtic sea salt
1/2 tsp fresh ground pepper
1/2 tsp fish sauce

Directions...
Place all ingredients into a salad jar and shake vigorously. Use for coleslaw, marinades or drizzle on your salad greens.

Makes 10 servings
NUTRITIONAL COMPARISON (per serving)
Store bought Asian Dressing =
 160 calories, 3g fat, 0g protein, 4g carbs, 0g fiber (4g effective carbs)
"Healthified" Asian Dressing =
160 calories, 3g fat, 0g protein, 0.2g carbs, 0g fiber (0.2g effective carbs)

NEW ITEMS

COCONUT VINEGAR nutritionally exceeds other vinegars in its amino acid, vitamin and mineral contents, and is an excellent source of FOS (a prebiotic that promotes digestive health). In addition to using in your favorite dressings and marinades, our Coconut Vinegar may also be used instead of apple cider vinegar for skincare or with any internal cleansing program. (This vinegar does not have a coconutty flavor.)

FISH SAUCE, mushrooms and aged cheeses have something called "UMAMI." Umami is a pleasant savory taste produced by glutamate and ribonucleotides, chemicals which occur naturally in many foods. Umami is subtle and not generally identified by people when they encounter it, but blends well with other tastes to intensify and enhance flavors; it plays an important role in making food taste delicious.

31

"HEALTHIFIED" SWEET MISO

"HEALTHIFIED" GARLIC OREGANO

"HEALTHIFIED" WARM BACON-MUSHROOM VINAIGRETTE

"HEALTHIFIED" GREEN GODDESS DRESSING

Ingredients:

"HEALTHIFIED" GREEN GODDESS DRESSING

1/2 c. avocado or organic mayo
1/2 c. organic buttermilk or coconut milk
   (more if you desire a thinner dressing)
1/4 c. chopped fresh chives
1/4 c. coarsely chopped flat-leaf parsley
1 TBS chopped fresh tarragon
1 TBS lemon juice
2 anchovy fillets (drained, chopped)
1 chopped garlic clove
Celtic sea salt and freshly ground black pepper

Directions...
In a processor, purée the first 8 ingredients until smooth. Season with kosher salt and freshly ground black pepper. Can be made 2 hours ahead. Cover and chill.

Makes 1 1/4 cup. NUTRITIONAL COMPARISON (per 2 TBS)

Traditional Dressing =
155 calories, 15g fat, 0.5g protein, 4.7g carbs, 0g fiber (4.7g effective carbs)

"Healthified" Avocado Dressing =
19 calories, 1.3g fat, 0.9g protein, 1.4g carbs, 0.5g fiber (0.9g effective carbs)

"Healthified" Mayo Dressing =
53 calories, 4.1g fat, 0.8g protein, 3.5g carbs, 0g fiber (3.5g effective carbs)

"HEALTHIFIED" WARM BACON-MUSHROOM VINAIGRETTE

4 oz. bacon (about 4 slices)
2 c. sliced mushrooms
3 TBS coconut vinegar
1/4 c. water
2 TBS macadamia nut OR quality olive oil
Celtic sea salt and freshly ground black pepper
2 TBS chopped flat-leaf parsley

Cut bacon into 1/2"-wide strips. Cook bacon with 3 TBS water in a medium skillet over medium heat, stirring often, until bacon starts to crisp. Add mushrooms; cook, tossing occasionally, until tender, about 5–6 minutes. Add vinegar and 1/4 cup water; simmer until reduced by half, about 1 minute. Stir in oil. Season with salt and freshly ground black pepper. Stir in parsley. Can be made 1 day ahead. Rewarm before using.

Makes 1 cup. NUTRITIONAL INFO (per 2 TBS)

Traditional Dressing =
140 calories, 14g fat, 1.2g protein, 5g carbs, 0g fiber (5 effective carbs)

"Healthified Dressing =
56 calories, 4.7g fat, 2.9g protein, 0.4g carbs, 0g fiber (0.4 effective carbs)

"HEALTHIFIED" GARLIC OREGANO

2 garlic cloves
2 anchovy fillets (drained)
1/2 tsp crushed red pepper flakes
Pinch of Celtic sea salt plus more
1/2 lime or lemon, seeded and finely chopped
   (with peel)
1/4 c. (loosely packed) fresh oregano leaves
1/4 c. macadamia nut or extra-virgin olive oil
Fresh lime or lemon juice

Finely chop garlic, anchovy fillets, red pepper flakes, and salt in a mini-processor. Add lemon and oregano; pulse a few times to coarsely chop. Add oil; process until a coarse purée forms. Season with more salt and fresh lime or lemon juice, if desired. Can be made 2 days ahead. Cover and chill. This assertive dressing loves hearty greens, chicken, steak and lamb.

Makes 1 cup, NUTRITIONAL INFO (per 2 TBS)
Traditional Dressing -
130 calories, 6g fat, 0.2g protein, 5g carbs, trace fiber (5g effective carbs)
"Healthified" Dressing = 41 calories, 3.5g fat, 1g protein, 2.6g carbs, 1.4g fiber (1.2g effective carbs)

"HEALTHIFIED" SWEET MISO

1/2 c. white miso
6 TBS macadamia nut oil
1/4 c. (packed) finely grated peeled zucchini
2 TBS finely grated peeled ginger
2 TBS unseasoned rice vinegar
4 tsp toasted sesame seeds
2 tsp sesame oil
2 tsp Nature's Hollow honey OR Swerve

Place all ingredients plus 1/4 cup water in a resealable container. Cover and shake vigorously until well combined. Can be made 2 days ahead. Cover and chill.

Makes 1 1/2 cups. NUTRITIONAL COMPARISON (per 2 TBS)

Traditional Sweet Miso Dressing =
125 calories, 8g fat, 1.6g protein, 8g carbs, 0.8g fiber (7.2g effective carbs)

"Healthified" Miso Dressing =
96 calories, 8g fat, 1.6g protein, 3.3g carbs, 0.8g fiber (2.5g effective carbs)

Quick Tip

There are so many seemingly harmless foods on the market, for the sake of our health, we all need to be food detectives. Our health depends on it. When I ask clients about their food diary, some say "a salad" for lunch, BUT when we inventory each item on the salad, serious issues arise. Even if you consume a salad of organic greens, farm fresh hard boiled eggs, "salad toppers" and homemade olive oil dressing...I'll say "stop!"... check out the ingredients on the "salad toppers!"

Those "toppers" have the caramel food coloring (banned in other countries), sugar, TRANS-FAT and soy. Soybeans raise a couple of issues (not to mention that non organic varieties are grown by MANSANTO and contain Round Up...I'm not putting that in my body). One problem is phytic acid, also called phytates. This is an organic acid (found in the hulls of all wheat) which block the body's ability to absorb minerals like calcium, magnesium, iron and especially zinc. A magnesium deficiency causes many issues like chocolate cravings, sleep issues, restless leg syndrome, headaches and migraines. An iron deficiency causes lack of energy and is the biggest issue for weight gain. A zinc deficiency can cause thyroid issues, acne on the face or back and cravings for something sweet after a meal or intense salty cravings.

Soybeans also contain enzyme inhibitors called trypsin which block absorption of enzymes that the body needs for protein digestion and can cause serious gastric distress, reduced protein digestion and can lead to chronic deficiencies in amino acid uptake (causing depression and other mood disorders AND a decrease in muscle tone). Soybeans also contain a clot-promoting substance called hemagglutinin, that causes red blood cells to clump together. These blood cells are unable to absorb oxygen for distribution to the cell's mitochondria (this is how we burn fat when we exercise) and is detrimental for cardiac health. The trypsin and hemagglutinin are "growth depressants." Which is why soy formula is so bad for babies. Only after a long period of fermentation (as in the creation of miso or tempeh) are the phytate and "antinutrient" levels of soybeans reduced which is why I use organic Tamari sauce...a truly fermented soy sauce.

Never use....
pre-made pie crusts or Saltine crackers because they have trans fats in them.

Shown left:
Chili with Crackers

Chili recipe on page 59.

Salad Toppers

Ingredients:

1 c. raw sunflower kernels
2/3 c. slivered almonds
1/4 c. almond flour
2 TBS chia seeds
1/4 c. sesame seeds
1 tsp Celtic sea salt
1 egg

Try flavored options
to the right

GARLIC HERB Option, add in...
1 tsp garlic powder
1/2 tsp red pepper flakes
1 tsp Paprika
1 tsp Italian herbs

SWEET CINNAMON Option, add in...
3 TBS erythritol
2 TBS unsweetened coconut flakes
1 tsp cinnamon
1/2 tsp ground nutmeg
1/4 tsp ground cloves (optional)

Directions... Preheat oven to 300 degrees F. In a shallow baking pan, toss the nuts, seeds, almond flour and salt with the egg. Add your desired spice by selecting one of the options below or by creating your own flavor. Mix until well incorporated. If you want a stronger flavor, add additional spices or sweetener. Spread the mixture as thin as possible onto your prepared baking sheet (wet hands and use fingers to spread it). Bake for 15 minutes. Remove from oven. Break up the pieces, flip and bake for an additional 5 minutes. Allow to cool.

NUTRITIONAL COMPARISON (per 3 TBS serving)
McCormick's = 70 calories, 4g fat, 0.9g protein, 4g carbs, 1.9g fiber (2.1g effective carbs)
"Healthified" Toppers = 65 calories, 4g fat, 2g protein, 3.8g carbs, 2.3g fiber (AND NO Trans-FAT!) (1.5g effective carbs)

Croutons

Ingredients:

BREAD:
5 eggs, separated
1/2 tsp cream of tartar
3 oz. sour cream
1/2 c. unflavored whey protein

CROUTONS:
1 batch of protein buns,
      cut into crouton shapes
4 TBS butter
1-2 tsp garlic, minced

Directions... Preheat oven to 375 degrees F. Separate the eggs and add sour cream to the yolks. Use a mixer to combine the ingredients. In a separate bowl, whip egg whites and cream of tartar until stiff. Using a spatula, gradually fold the sour cream into the white mixture, being careful not to break down the whites. Spray a cookie sheet with coconut oil spray and spoon the mixture onto the sheet, making 6 mounds. Bake at 375 degrees F for 18 minutes. Turn the oven off. Keep oven shut, and leave the buns in there for another 5 minutes or until cool. Preheat oven to 350 degrees F. Place the butter in a sauté pan on medium heat until slightly brown, add the garlic and bread pieces to coat. Place buttery croutons on baking sheet and bake for 15 minutes or until crispy. Let cool and enjoy!

NUTRITIONAL COMPARISON (per 1 cup):
Pepperidge Farm Seasoned Croutons = 186 calories, 2g fat, 4.3g protein, 25.4g carbs, 2g fiber (23.4g effective carbs)
"Healthified" Croutons = 162 Calories, 2g fat, 6.3g protein, 0.9g carbs, 0g fiber (0.9g effective carbs)

There are many reasons for hair loss; most of which links back to nutrition. Here are just a few:

1. Alopecia (discussed in my book, "Art of Eating Healthy: Sweets") is an auto-immune disease which is directly linked to food allergies.

2. Iron Deficiency: This can happen a few ways: not eating foods containing iron, heavy menstruation, heavy exercise, OR you aren't absorbing iron due to a food allergy/sensitivity/leaky gut.

3. DHT (Testosterone by-product): This can happen with men AND women. This is when testosterone is converted to DHT (dihydro-testosterone). Nearly half of all men have an inherited gene that makes them at risk of losing their hair because too much of the testosterone in their body is getting converted to DHT and resulting in low actual testosterone. The key is to take steps before it becomes a problem.

How do we fix it?

1. Healthy Fats and CHOLESTEROL: Salmon, nuts, avocado, peanut butter, coconut oil. Eggs and butter are also very important because cholesterol is essential in creating important hormones like androgen, testosterone, estrogen and progesterone. Cholesterol is also important for reproduction; it brings out male and female sexual characteristics. These essential nutrients are especially beneficial for children and expectant mothers. As the use of butter in America has declined, sterility rates and problems with sexual development have increased. When animals consume butter substitutes, their growth is stunted and they are unable to sustain reproduction.

2. Zinc: A deficiency in zinc can cause a 75% drop in testosterone. Zinc supplements can cause testosterone levels to double if deficient and can increase sperm production in men. Zinc is found in pasture-fed meats, chicken, yolks of eggs, oysters, crab, pine nuts and cheese.

3. Vitamin E: Vitamin E is a FAT-SOLUBLE vitamin; if you have been eating a low-fat or no-fat diet and are losing your hair, this is most likely the cause. I love almond flour because it has tons of vitamin E. Sunflower seeds, asparagus, avocado, olives, spinach and other green leafy vegetables are good sources to consume in large quantities.

4. Allicin: RAW garlic contains the highest concentration of this testosterone-boosting compound, cooking diminishes the effects. It also decreases cortisol, which competes with testosterone and interferes with its normal function. Add garlic and onions to your meals to stimulate testosterone's production.

5. Coniferous Veggies: Diindolylmethane, is a natural phytonutrient in coniferous vegetables (cauliflower, cabbage, broccoli, Brussels sprouts) which limits the effects of male estrogen. These veggies contain nutrients called indoles. Indoles lowers estrogen which also competes with testosterone production.

6. Protein: Eating protein after intense exercise has been shown to increase the amount of testosterone that enters muscle cells which stimulates muscle growth. Choose quality protein, and try supplementing with one or two whey protein shakes per day (especially after exercise).

7. B Vitamins: Studies show that consumption of B Vitamins directly correlates with an increase in testosterone. Meat, poultry and fish contain lots of B vitamins. Vegetarians should be sure to take a b-complex vitamin.

8. Caffeine: High amounts of caffeine added to exercise can increase testosterone production. Yet don't overindulge. Stick to 200-400mg of caffeine a day and keep caffeine away from bed-time. Sleep is just as important to testosterone.

9. Niacin: Studies show that niacin increases HDL; which directly links to a higher testosterone production. Increase niacin by including meat, poultry, fish, nuts, eggs and quality dairy products.

10. High Intensity Exercise: After about 20 minutes into an exercise session, blood levels of testosterone increase and remain elevated for up to three hours after exercise. Maintain muscle with consistent strength training.

Reduce Testosterone With:

1. Alcohol: Drinking alcohol increases estrogen by 300% (enter hot-flashes); which in turn decreases testosterone (enter "beer belly" and erectile dysfunction).

2. Low-fat diet: A low-fat diet nullifies the typical increase in testosterone after resistance training. Testosterone is made from cholesterol, which is a form of fat. Include a balance of fat and protein after a tough workout.

3. Low-protein diet: Low-protein diets increase sex hormone-binding globulin (SHBG) levels; which attaches to hormones and makes them unavailable for our body. An increase in SHBG decreases usable testosterone. Always include a protein at every meal and snack.

4. Phytoestrogens: Phytoestrogens mimic estrogen, which in turn decreases testosterone. Phytoestrogens are found in flaxseeds and soy products; keep these to a minimum.

5. Lack of sleep and too much stress: Getting less than 7 hours of sleep a night decreases the production of testosterone. An increase in stress boosts the secretion of cortisol; which overshadows the production of testosterone. Get sufficient sleep and reduce stress.

Kale Chips

Ingredients:

1 head kale, rinsed and dried
Coconut oil spray
Celtic sea salt

OPTIONAL:
Parmesan Cheese

Directions...
Preheat oven to 250 degrees F. Using a knife, remove the thick inner stems from the leaves, leaving long strips; cut the strips in half. Arrange the leaves dark side up in a single layer on two baking sheets. Lightly mist each piece with coconut oil spray. Sprinkle with salt OR Parmesan cheese. Bake about 20 minutes, until kale is crisp and cheese is golden.

NUTRITIONAL Information (per cup)
Microwave Popcorn =
160 calories, 9g fat, 3g protein, 18g carbs, 3g fiber (15g effective carbs)
Kale Chips =
34 calories, 0.5g fat, 2.3g protein, 6g carbs, 1.5g fiber (4.5g effective carbs)

Use Kale Chips on sandwiches
for a healthy crunch.

Grilled Romaine

Ingredients:

2 heads romaine lettuce
Macadamia nut OR quality olive oil
Warm Bacon-Mushroom Vinaigrette, recipe page 33

OPTIONAL ADDITIONS:
Walnuts, tomatoes, grilled grass fed steak,
blue cheese, marinated red peppers

Directions...
Preheat a grill to medium-high. Rinse and pat dry the lettuce. Cut the 2 heads in half lengthwise. Brush surface with oil and grill about 4 to 5 minutes total, turning occasionally. Place each wedge on a salad plate and drizzle with dressing. Top with your favorite additions and serve.

Makes 4 servings
NUTRITIONAL INFORMATION
Grilled Romaine = 124 calories, 4g fat, 2g protein,
3g carbs, 1g fiber (2g effective carbs)

Tuna "Noodle" Salad

Ingredients:

1 jar Hearts of Palm
1/4 c. chopped dill pickles
1 stalk celery, chopped
1 (12 oz.) can tuna
1/2 c. Spectrum Mayo
1 pinch of Celtic sea salt

OPTIONAL: Hard Boiled Eggs and a handful of peas.

Directions...
Cut up the Hearts of Palm into "noodle-like" shapes. In a large bowl, combine the Hearts of Palm pieces, pickles, celery and tuna. Prepare the dressing by whisking together the mayonnaise and salt. Add to tuna mixture. Top with hard boiled eggs and peas if desired. Cover and refrigerate for 1 hour.

Serves 4. NUTRITIONAL COMPARISON (per serving)
Traditional Salad = 260 calories, 5g fat, 9g protein, 35.8g carbs, 2g fiber (33.8g effective carbs)
"Healthified" Salad = 124 calories, 5g fat, 12g protein, 6g carbs, 2g fiber (4g effective carbs)

NEW INGREDIENT: **Hearts of Palm** is a great veggie to substitute for noodles. They are from the inner portion of the palm tree. Hearts of palm are ivory-colored and delicately flavored. Their texture is smooth and a little firm with a flavor that

Asparagus Crab Salad

Ingredients:

2 pounds fresh asparagus spears, trimmed
4 red peppers, sliced
1/2 pound nitrate-free bacon strips, diced
1 pint grape tomatoes
Celtic sea salt and pepper to taste
1 clove garlic, minced
1 pound crab meat, flaked (I found mine at Sam's)
2 TBS freshly squeezed lemon juice
3 TBS macadamia nut or olive oil
1 clove garlic, minced

OPTIONAL: hard boiled eggs

Directions...
Cut the asparagus and peppers into 2 inch pieces. Cook the bacon in a large, deep skillet over medium-high heat until crisp, about 10 minutes. Add in the asparagus, peppers, tomatoes, crab to the bacon (and grease from the bacon) and cook until veggies are crisp tender. Transfer to a large mixing bowl. Whisk the lemon juice, oil, and 1 minced clove garlic together in a small bowl; season with salt and pepper. Pour the dressing over the salad and toss to coat.

Makes 10 servings. NUTRITIONAL COMPARISON (per serving)
Using Imitation Crab = 173 calories, 3g fat, 4g protein, 13g carbs, 2.8g fiber (10.2g effective carbs)
"Healthified" Salad = 163 calories, 3g fat, 12g protein, 6g carbs, 2.8g fiber (3.2g effective carbs)

Another question I am frequently asked is about quinoa. Yes, it is higher in protein than most grains, but for those with a damaged metabolism or anyone who wants to lose weight, it is way too high in carbs... just check out the nutritional comparison at the end of the recipe... the numbers don't lie!

We all know that sugar is bad, but we mistakenly believe complex carbohydrates are healthy and we need to eat them in abundance. BUT what if I told you that "Complex carbohydrates" and "Whole Grains" are just glucose molecules hooked together in a long chain; the digestive track breaks it down into glucose...also known as sugar. So a "complex carb" diet and a "sugary" diet are pretty much the same thing.

"Quinoa" Greek Salad

Ingredients:

2 packages Miracle Rice
1 1/2 TBS butter or coconut oil, softened
1 red chili, de-seeded and finely chopped
   (optional)
1 garlic clove, crushed
2 chicken breasts
2 tsp coconut oil
1 tomato, roughly chopped
1/4 c. pitted black kalamata olives
1 red onion, finely sliced
1/2 c. feta cheese, crumbled
2 TBS mint leaves, chopped
1 lemon, juiced and some of the zest

Directions...

Drain the Miracle Rice, rinse well and set aside. In a small bowl, mix the butter, chili and garlic into a paste. Rub the chicken breasts in 2 tsp of the oil. Lay in a hot griddle pan and cook for 3-4 mins each side or until cooked through. Transfer to a plate, dot with the spicy butter and set aside to melt. Next, place the tomatoes, olives, onion, feta and mint into a bowl. Toss in the Miracle Rice. Stir in the lemon juice and zest, and season well. Serve with the chicken fillets on top, drizzled with buttery chicken juices. Optional: drizzle with additional Greek dressing.

Makes 4 servings.
NUTRITIONAL COMPARISON (per serving)

Traditional Quinoa =
436 calories, 16.9g fat, 39.4g protein, 31g carbs, 3g fiber (28g effective carbs)
"Healthified" Quinoa =
288 calories, 14g fat, 33.8g protein, 4.8g carbs, 1.1g fiber (3.7g effective carbs)

DID YOU KNOW?

"Complex carbohydrates" and "Whole Grains" are just glucose molecules hooked together in a long chain; the digestive track breaks it down into glucose... also known as sugar. (see caption above)

The Healthy Substitute

In this recipe I swapped out the heavy cream, skim milk and sugar with cream cheese, chicken broth and stevia. This cut a lot of calories, yet kept a lot of flavor. I LOVE this soup. I often add some baby lobster pieces from Trader Joe's to make a filling lunch.

Gorgonzola Bisque

Ingredients:

1 TBS butter or coconut oil
¼ large red onion, diced
½ c. red bell pepper, diced
2 cloves garlic, minced
¼ c. Gorgonzola cheese, crumbled
4 oz. cream cheese, softened
1 c. veggie/chicken broth
1 (14.5 oz.) diced tomatoes
1 ½ c. tomato sauce
2 tsp dried basil
1/4 tsp stevia glycerite (or to taste)
¼ tsp pepper

Directions...

Heat oil in a medium saucepan over medium heat. Add the onion, pepper, and garlic; cook and stir 4 to 5 minutes or until vegetables are soft. Add the cheeses and broth; heat mixture until cheeses melt and the mixture is simmering. Stir in the tomatoes (including their liquid), tomato sauce, basil, stevia, and pepper. Continue to simmer mixture for 15 to 20 minutes while stirring constantly. Do not boil.

OPTION:
Cool soup a bit and puree it until smooth, then return to heat.
Top with a Parmesan crisp!

Makes 4 servings.
NUTRITIONAL COMPARISON (per serving)

Traditional Soup =
257 calories, 10g fat. 2g protein,14.3g carbs, 2.2g fiber (13.1g effective carbs)

"Healthified" Soup =

Basil

FUN HERB FACT

Dill contains calcium and iron, and the oils in the plant may help to neutralize carcinogens, which are substances that have been shown to cause cancer. Dill also has a number of beneficial healing properties for the digestive system and has been used since ancient times to treat heartburn and also diarrhea.

Ingredients:

1/2 c. chopped onion
2 stalks celery, chopped
1/4 c. butter or coconut oil
1 1/2 tsp garam masala (or curry)
4 c. chicken broth
1/2 c. jicama, chopped
1/4 c. cauliflower "rice"
1 chicken breast, cubed
Celtic sea salt to taste
Fresh ground black pepper to taste
1 pinch dried thyme
1/2 c. coconut milk (or more
    if you want a creamier soup)

Directions... Fry onions and celery in butter in a large soup pot. Add garam masala spice (or curry), and cook 5 more minutes. Add chicken stock, mix well, and bring to a boil. Simmer about 1/2 hour. Add jicama, cauliflower "rice", chicken, salt, pepper, and thyme. CAULIFLOWER "RICE": Place the cauliflower heads into a food processor, pulse until small pieces of "rice." Simmer 15-20 minutes. When serving, add hot coconut milk.

Makes 6 servings.
NUTRITIONAL COMPARISON (per serving)
Using Cream/Rice/Apple = 213 calories, 16g fat, 6.2g protein, 13g carbs, 1.4g fiber (11.6g effective carbs)
Using Coconut Milk/Cauliflower/Jicama = 171 calories, 13 g fat, 7.9g protein, 3.8g carbs, 1.4g fiber (2.4g effective carbs)

A Heartwarming Favorite...
Curl up with a warm bowl of soup
to make the perfect ending to your day.

Bone broths are one of the most nourishing foods. It is so medicinal that if I could sell it in a pill form, the pharmaceutical companies would be broke. Because broth can be regarded as a liquefied form of the important components of bones, the medicinal benefits of bone broth are attributed to the exceptionally high levels of minerals and amino acids. In fact bone broth can be considered both a high quality multi-mineral and protein supplement.

1. HYDROPHILIC COLLOIDS: Stock is also awesome because it has hydrophilic colloids. Raw foods are colloidal and are hydrophilic, meaning that they attract liquids. This is important because when we eat a salad or other raw food, the hydrophilic colloids attract digestive juices for rapid and effective digestion. Colloids that have been heated are usually hydrophobic (meaning they repel liquids, making cooked foods harder to digest). However, the gelatin in meat broths has the special property of attracting liquids even after it has been heated. A good visual is Jell-O - the gelatin attracts water to form desserts, which allows it to attract digestive juices to the surface of cooked food particles.

2. CROHN'S and COLITIS: Broth contains gelatin, which aids in digestion and works amazing as a treatment of intestinal disorders, including hyperacidity, colitis and Crohn's disease because it heals the intestinal wall. Many clients of mine have Colitis, leaky gut, diverticulitis, Crohn's or other intestinal problems. By supplementing with broth and other key supplements (such as l-glutamine) we can strengthen the intestinal walls, which also supports our immune system. Babies had fewer digestive problems when gelatin was added to their milk. It enhances digestion by attracting digestive juices to food in the gut. It also calms and soothes the gut lining. Gelatin should be the first therapeutic food for anyone suffering from digestive conditions affecting the intestines.

3. Collagen is a protein extracted in broth through the breakdown of bone and cartilage during the cooking process and is referred to as gelatin. The quality of broth is usually determined by the amount of gelatin it contains. The gelatin in broth is also useful for the treatment of anemia and other blood disorders, like diabetes, muscular dystrophy and even cancer.

4. AMINO ACIDS: Although gelatin isn't a complete protein, (it only has the amino acids arginine and glycine in large amounts) it acts as a protein sparer, allowing the body to more fully utilize the complete proteins that are taken in. So if you are someone who can't afford large amounts of meat in your diet, gelatin-rich broths are great to help boost protein absorption.

5. MINERAL ABSORPTION: Healthy bone tissue is naturally high in minerals (calcium, magnesium, phosphorus, potassium) which provide a healthy bone structure, nervous system and hormone balance. Fish stock will also provide iodine which is essential for a healthy thyroid. Broths made from fish bones will also provide iodine. The gelatin in broth strengthens digestion which helps you absorb more nutrients. Gelatin helps people digest milk and dairy products.

"Stock contains minerals in a form the body can absorb easily—not just calcium but also magnesium, phosphorus, silicon, sulphur and trace minerals. It contains the broken down material from cartilage and tendons - stuff like chondroitin sulphates and glucosamine, now sold as expensive supplements for arthritis and joint pain." Sally Fallon Morell

6. JOINT HEALTH: Since the gelatin is derived from cartilage, a huge benefit of broth is that it provides an awesome source of glucosamine and chondroitin. These nutrients are essential for regaining joint health.

NOTE: When making bone broth, you must add an acid like organic COCONUT vinegar to help extract more minerals from the bones. The extracted minerals then become the alkalinizing agents to neutralize the acidity of the broth. Coconut Vinegar nutritionally exceeds other vinegars in its amino acid, vitamin and mineral contents, and is an excellent source of FOS (a prebiotic that promotes digestive health). In addition to using in your favorite dressings and marinades, Coconut Vinegar may also be used instead of apple cider vinegar for skin care or with any internal cleansing program. (This vinegar does not have a "coconutty" flavor.)

Chicken "Noodle" Soup

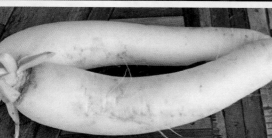

Daikon = A radish vegetable with minimal taste. A one cup serving of daikon contains about 20 calories, 4g carbs and 2g of fiber for an effective carb count of 2g. Daikon are an excellent source of vitamin C and has lots of magnesium, folate, and provides 10% of your RDA for fiber. Zucchini will also work in this soup, but it doesn't hold up well if leftover.

Ingredients:

4 c. chopped, cooked chicken meat
1 c. chopped celery
1/4 c. chopped onion
1/4 c. butter or coconut oil
4 c. Daikon or zucchini (cut into noodle shapes)
12 c. chicken broth
1/2 tsp dried marjoram
3 slices fresh ginger root
1/2 tsp ground black pepper
1 bay leaf
1 TBS dried parsley

Directions... Peel and cut daikon or zucchini with the veggie cutter (see below) or by hand to resemble noodles. In a large stock pot, sauté celery and onion in butter until soft. Add chicken, chicken broth, marjoram, ginger, black pepper, bay leaf, and parsley. Simmer for 30 minutes. Add daikon or zucchini, and simmer for 10 more minutes.

NOTE: daikon makes better leftovers, zucchini gets a bit too soft.

Makes 10 servings. NUTRITIONAL COMPARISON (per serving)
Traditional Soup = 227 calories, 8g fat, 24g protein, 19g carbs, 2g fiber (17g effective carbs)
"Healthified" Soup = 120 calories, 8g fat, 24g protein, 4g carbs, 2g fiber (2g effective carbs)

The "NOODLE" Maker can be found here: http://astore.amazon.com/marisnutran05-20/detail/B0000DDVYE

Ramen

Ingredients:

4 c. zucchini "noodles"
3 1/2 c. vegetable broth
2 tsp organic Tamari sauce (soy sauce)
1/2 tsp minced fresh ginger root
1/2 tsp chili oil (or sesame oil)

1 egg, lightly beaten
2 green onions, sliced

OPTIONAL: 4 soft boiled eggs and sautéed purple cabbage

Directions... Peel and "swirl" the zucchini using The Spiral Slicer (see the link above showing where you can buy it). In a medium saucepan combine broth, zucchini noodles, tamari sauce and ginger. Simmer, uncovered, for 10 minutes. Stir in chili or sesame oil. Slowly pour in the egg and stir for 30 seconds until the egg has cooked. Garnish with green onions and a soft boiled egg and cabbage if desired.

Makes 4 servings. NUTRITIONAL COMPARISON (per serving)
Traditional Ramen = 190 calories, 2g fat, 4g protein, 26g carbs, 2g fiber (24g effective carbs)
"Healthified" Ramen = 75 calories, 2g fat, 9g protein, 5.3g carbs, 1.4g fiber (3.9g effective carbs)
To find the Spiral Slicer: http://astore.amazon.com/marisnutran05-20/detail/B0000DDVYE

Cream of Mushroom Soup

Ingredients:

1 lb button mushrooms, cleaned and sliced
1 TBS lemon juice
1 TBS butter
2 TBS minced shallots
1 tsp dried thyme
1/2 bay leaf
1 tsp Celtic sea salt
1/2 tsp fresh ground pepper
4 oz. cream cheese
2 c. veggie/chicken broth

Directions... In a food processor, coarsely chop mushrooms in lemon juice. Melt butter in a saucepan and lightly sauté shallots on medium heat. Add mushrooms, thyme and bay leaf, sauté over moderate heat for 10-15 minutes, or until the liquid that is released from the mushrooms disappears. Add salt, pepper, cream cheese and chicken stock and bring to boil. Reduce heat and simmer for 20 minutes. Stirring constantly. Correct seasoning and add more lemon juice to taste.

Makes 4 servings.
NUTRITIONAL COMPARISON (per serving)
Campbell's Soup =
166 calories, 10g fat, 6.2g protein, 14g carbs, 2g fiber (12g effective carbs)
"Healthified" Soup =
155 calories, 13g fat, 6.4g protein, 5.9g carbs, 1.3g fiber (4.6g effective carbs)

A Healthy Relationship...

A healthy substitute to the store bought version
that your waistline will definitely get along with.

Chicken Dumpling Soup

Ingredients:

4 quarts water (reverse osmosis
    filtered water is best)
1 pasture fed chicken
1 whole clove fresh garlic,
    peeled & smashed
2 TBS coconut or apple cider vinegar
    (see page 31)
2 TBS coconut oil
2 onions, diced
2 stalks celery, sliced 1/4 inch thick
1 tsp thyme leaves

DUMPLINGS:
4 eggs (2 eggs if using almond flour)
1 tsp Celtic sea salt
1 c. coconut flour
    (OR 2 c. almond flour)
2 TBS psyllium husk powder
1/4 tsp thyme

IF USING COCONUT FLOUR:
1/2 c. chicken broth

Directions...
Place the water, chicken, garlic, and vinegar in a large kettle or a large crockpot and set the heat to "high." Bring to a boil, then reduce the setting to "low" for a soft simmer. Cook for a minimum of 8 hours and up to 24 hours. The longer it cooks the more nutrients and minerals!

Strain broth through a colander into a large container; reserve broth and discard skin and bones. Return kettle or crockpot to burner set on medium-high. Add oil, then onions and celery. Sauté about 8 to 10 minutes or until tender. Add chicken, broth and thyme. Bring to a simmer.

DUMPLINGS: In a medium sized bowl, mix the eggs, salt, flour, psyllium powder, and thyme, mix until sticky and well-blended. For coconut flour dumplings add a little broth until the dough sticks together. Shape into dumplings with hands. Note: These can be made ahead and frozen until you are ready for some soup!

With the soup at a simmer, add the dumplings. Cover the soup and cook for 20-30 minutes. Season to taste with salt and pepper. Enjoy!

Makes 8 servings. NUTRITIONAL COMPARISON (per serving)
Traditional Soup =
330 calories, 10g fat, 25g protein, 31g carbs, 2.2g fiber (28.8g effective carbs)
Almond Flour Dumpling Soup =
363 calories, 22g fat, 29g protein, 9.7g carbs, 3.5g fiber (6.2g effective carbs)
Coconut Flour Dumpling Soup =
291 calories, 12g fat, 28g protein, 11g carbs, 5g fiber (6g effective carbs)

Even one gram
of trans-fat is
terrible for our
metabolism and
it take 9 months
to detox from
our body!

DID YOU KNOW?

Consuming MSG
triples the amount
of insulin that the
pancreas creates.
AND
excess insulin
equals obesity.

MSG

Here is another item to toss from your pantry! What is that gelatinous goo anyway?

Ingredients: Water, Mushrooms, Vegetable Oil (Corn, Cottonseed, Canola and/or Soybean)Modified Food Starch, Wheat Flour, contains Less than 2% of: Cream (Milk) Salt, Dried Whey (Milk)Monosodium Glutamate, Soy Protein Concentrate, Yeast Extract, Spice Extract, Dehydrated Garlic.

MSG is a slow poison and it is in everything; Lay's potato chips, Doritos, Campbell's soups, Ramen, canned gravy, frozen dinners, frozen pizzas, salad dressings (especially low-fat varieties). Tons of 'reduced' or 'no-fat' foods are laced with MSG to make up for flavor lost when fat is reduced. If you don't see MSG on the label, you still aren't safe; the words 'Hydrolyzed Vegetable Protein','Accent, 'Aginomoto,' 'Natural Meat Tenderizer,' are just sneaky names for MSG.

Glutamic acid in MSG is known as an excitotoxin; this means it excites the brain cells. It causes the brain cells to fire too much until they are exhausted and die. This causes us to be addicted to the MSG 'fix,' which is why Lay's Potato Chips claim, "I bet you can't eat just one." Lay's knows they have the upper hand on your brain chemistry. This excitotoxin effect in our brain causes ADHD, autism and Alzheimer's.

This process of over-exciting the brain depletes our brain of serotonin (the feel-good chemical in our brain and gut). Headaches and migraines are the main complaint of MSG consumption, which makes sense because low serotonin is a main cause of these painful headaches and MSG causes a drastic change in the level of serotonin. Serotonin plays many roles in the body, one of which is the effect on blood vessels. When serotonin levels are high, blood vessels constrict (shrink). When serotonin levels fall, the blood vessels dilate (swell). This swelling can cause pain or other problems. Many things can affect the level of serotonin in your body, including your level of blood sugar, certain foods and changes in your estrogen level if you're a woman. To read more check out my book, Secrets to Controlling Your Cravings, Weight and Mood.

MSG down regulates our body's leptin production (our appetite suppression), so it makes us hungry sooner. How can this be? Well, MSG stimulates the pancreas, which in turn increases insulin production even though there is no need for insulin. This will cause our blood sugar to rise too much and then drop. When our blood sugar drops, hunger is stimulated (which is why you don't want to eat too many carbohydrates either). Over-production of insulin will cause insulin resistance, diabetes and obesity.

Bread Bowl Chowder

Ingredients:

BREAD BOWL:
1 1/4 c. blanched almond flour
    (or 1/2 c. coconut flour)
5 TBS psyllium husk powder (no substitutes)
2 tsp baking powder
1 tsp Celtic sea salt
2 egg whites (8 egg whites if using coconut flour)
1 c. BOILING water (or broth- for extra flavor)

CHOWDER:
1/2 c. butter
1/2 c. onion, chopped
1 c. celery, diced
2 c. cauliflower flowerets
3 c. broth (veggie or chicken)
4 oz. cream cheese or mascarpone cheese
1 tsp Celtic sea salt
2 (6.5 oz.) cans clams, drained
1/4 tsp psyllium powder (for thickening)

OPTIONAL:
4 slices of bacon, into small pieces

Directions...

Preheat the oven to 350 degrees F. In a medium sized bowl, combine the almond, psyllium powder (no substitutes: flaxseed meal won't work), baking powder and salt. Add in the eggs and combine until a thick dough. Add boiling water into the bowl. Mix until well combined. Divide the dough into 4 balls. Place on a baking sheet and bake for 65 minutes or until golden brown. Once totally cool, cut the top of the bread bowl off to fill with soup.

Place the butter in a saucepan and heat on high until brown specks appear, making "brown butter." Turn on medium heat and add the onion, celery and cauliflower (and bacon if using). Sauté for 10 minutes or until the vegetables are tender (and bacon is cooked). Add in the broth and softened cream cheese (use a whisk to incorporate the cream cheese or little specks of cream cheese will be in the soup). Season with salt. Add in the clams. Whisk in the psyllium to desired thickness... a little goes a long way!

Makes 8 servings.
NUTRITIONAL COMPARISON (per serving)
Traditional Chowder Bowl =
480 calories, 19g fat, 12g protein, 77g carbs, 3g fiber (74g effective carbs)
"Healthified" Almond Flour Chowder =
309 calories, 23g fat, 10.6g protein, 10.5g carbs, 5.7g fiber (4.8g effective carbs)
"Healthified" Coconut Flour Chowder =
267 calories, 16g fat, 19.5g protein, 11g carbs, 6.2g fiber (4.8g effective carbs)

Popcorn = Weight Gain

By now, we all know we need to stay away from trans-fat for our health and to maximize weight loss...but do you know where to find it?

Pop-Secret Kettle Corn (4 cups popped)
180 calories
13 g fat (6 g trans)

The only "secret" here is that they use partially hydrogenated oil to pop their kernels, turning this snack into a nutritional nightmare of heart-wrenching proportions. This box has 3 bags of popcorn, which means every time you buy it, you're bringing 54 grams of dangerous trans fat into your house. There's not an easier—or more important—swap to make.

Another reason to switch out your bed-night snack of popcorn is that it is contributing to a stall in weight loss. In one popular low-fat diet program, they consider, 5 cups of air popped popcorn to = 1 point...Yeah, it is very low in calories, but it is ALL SUGAR! 38 grams of carbohydrates = 9.5 teaspoons of sugar in our blood, which is way too much. There is no fat to slow the insulin spike from happening (which is why I always use full fat real foods). Our brain neurotransmitters also get out of balance when we have chronic high insulin levels. Cravings, moodiness, depression, anxiety or fatigue are all caused by excess insulin causing blood sugar roller coasters.

This is how weight gain happens.
First, insulin tells your body to eat, particularly sugar or carbohydrates. If you follow cravings, insulin rewards you with extreme gratification (dopamine). Second, insulin escorts the energy from these foods, which is now blood sugar, to wherever it is needed in the body. It tells the liver to turn any extra carbohydrate into triglycerides, to be stored in the fat cells. And third, it orders the body to keep the food energy locked inside the fat cells, not burning it for energy, but storing it...increasing triglyceride levels!

A TIP ON EGGS:
I often get the question: Can I have eggs every day? How many eggs a day is safe? I have to tell you, I get a bit frustrated when I hear this. Especially when the person doesn't think twice about the cereal and skim milk they are feeding their little ones, which is filled with FOOD DYE, TBHQ, BHT, high fructose corn syrup/sugar, Genetically Modified CORN or SOYBEANS, the RANCID milk solids added to skim milk, the hormones and antibiotics in the milk ... OR not thinking twice about the ingredients in the breads they use, GMO corn syrup, trans-fat, refined flour...

MYTH: there's something unhealthy about cholesterol.
Cholesterol = body's repair substances
Its elevated presence = your body is healing something
Most Americans consume 200-300mg of cholesterol
We need 1000mg a day, liver makes the rest = unhealthy cholesterol
Cholesterol is essential for hormone function
Statin drugs = muscles deteriorate; which = slows metabolism.
Focusing on inflammatory foods: Processed, fried foods, LOW-FAT DAIRY, white bread, sugar

So, as for the eggs, I would focus more on getting all prepackaged foods out of my diet. I would also worry WAY more about the hormones and antibiotics in chicken, milk, and meat. We eat prepackaged foods with so many harmful chemical that are way worse than a natural egg. Mother's Breast milk from a healthy mother has about 50-60% of its calories as fat. The cholesterol in human milk supplies an infant with close to 6 times the amount most adults consume from their food. In China, a new mother is given a diet very high in cholesterol and animal fat; she consumes 6-10 eggs a day and almost 10 ounces of chicken and pork for at least a month after birth. This diet ensures that the level of fat in her milk is as high as possible; our brains are over 60% fat which is why Alzheimer's is now linked to low cholesterol diets!

Make popcorn shapes as pictured to the left or Cheeto-like shapes as pictured below.

Pop"corn"

Ingredients:

1/2 c. freshly shredded
    cheddar cheese (frozen)
3 egg whites
1/8 tsp cream of tartar
Parmesan cheese (if desired)

Directions...

Preheat oven to 300 degrees F. Put the frozen cheese in a food processor/blender and chop, until it's in tiny little pieces. In a mixing bowl, whip the whites with cream of tartar until VERY stiff peaks form. Sprinkle the chopped cheese, on top of the egg whites. Then, with a rubber spatula, fold the cheese into the egg whites, VERY CAREFULLY, being careful not to disturb the fluffy whites, but thoroughly spread the cheese, throughout.

Carefully place the mixture into a large Ziplock bag, cut a ½ inch hole in the corner of bag. Gently squeeze onto cookie sheet in popcorn (or Cheeto)-like shapes. I would suggest using a sheet of parchment baking paper, to line your pan, but if you don't, be sure to grease the pan. Lightly sprinkle grated parmesan cheese, on top of each puff.

Bake at 300 degrees F, for 20-30 minutes. The longer you can bake them (without them getting too brown), the crispier they will be. For even crispier puffs, turn off the oven, and leave them in the oven for at least 30-minutes. Store in a tightly sealed, air-tight container.

Makes 6 servings.
NUTRITIONAL COMPARISON (per serving)
Store Bought Cheetos = 160 calories, 6g fat, 0g protein, 15g carbs, 1g fiber (14g effective carbs)
"Healthified" Cheetos = 45 calories, 4g fat, 8g protein, trace carbs, 0g fiber (0g effective carbs)

Quick Tip

We have replaced feeding cows corn instead of grass to fatten them up in 6 months vs 2-3 years...
why don't people get the connection that corn will do the same thing to us?

These are an awesome appetizer to make ahead for an upcoming party. I made the "puffs" a week ahead and I stored in the freezer. I also made the filling a day ahead and kept in the fridge until just before serving.

Crab Rangoon Puffs

Ingredients:

PUFFS:
3 eggs, separated
1/2 tsp cream of tartar
1/2 c. unflavored whey or egg white protein
3 oz. sour cream or cream cheese, softened

CRAB RANGOON:
1 clove garlic, minced
1 (8 oz.) package cream cheese
1 (6 oz.) can crab meat, drained and flaked
2 green onions with tops, thinly sliced
1 tsp fresh ginger, finely grated
1/2 tsp organic Tamari (soy sauce)

EGG SALAD FILLING:
8 eggs
1 TBS homemade mayo OR
    Spectrum Organic Mayo
2 TBS Dijon-style mustard
1 tsp dried dill weed
1 tsp paprika
Celtic sea salt and pepper to taste

Directions...

Preheat oven to 375 degrees F. Separate the eggs and reserve the yolks for another recipe (creme brule anyone?). In a large bowl, whip egg whites and cream of tartar until VERY stiff. Then add the whey. Using a spatula, gradually fold the sour cream into the egg white mixture, being careful not to break down the whites. Place round balls of dough onto a GREASED baking sheet (or a mini muffin tin works great). Bake at 375 degrees F for 10 minutes. Keep oven shut, and leave the puffs in there for another 5 minutes or until cool. Makes 24 puffs.

NUTRITIONAL COMPARISON (per puff)
Traditional Egg Puffs = 47 calories, 6g fat, 0g protein, 7 carbs, trace fiber (7g effective carbs)
"Healthified" Egg Puffs = 21 calories, 2g fat, 3g protein, trace carbs, 0g fiber (0g effective carbs)

CRAB FILLING: Combine garlic, cream cheese, crab, green onions, ginger, and Tamari sauce in a bowl. Fill puffs. To prevent puffs from getting soggy, fill the day you plan on eating.

Makes 8 servings. NUTRITIONAL COMPARISON (per serving)
Traditional Crab Rangoon =
261 calories, 21g fat, 11g protein, 29.2 carbs, 1 fiber (28.2 effective carbs)
"Healthified" Crab Rangoon =
177.5 calories, 11g fat, 12g protein, 2.1 carbs, 1 fiber (1.1 effective carbs)

EGG SALAD FILLING: Place eggs in a saucepan and cover with cold water. Bring water to a boil; cover, remove from heat, and let eggs stand in hot water for 10 to 12 minutes. Remove from hot water, cool, peel and chop. In a large bowl, combine the egg, mayonnaise, mustard, dill, paprika, and salt and pepper. Mash well with a fork or wooden spoon.

Makes 4 servings. Per serving = 183 calories, 2.9 carbs, 0.5g fiber

Fried Green Tomatoes

Ingredients:

1/4 c. Coconut OR Macadamia Nut Oil
1 large tomato (green, yet soft)
1 egg
1/2 c. almond meal
1/2 tsp Celtic sea salt
Fresh ground pepper to taste

OPTIONAL:
fresh basil from the garden

Directions...
In a frying pan heat oil. Cut tomato into 1/4 inch slices. Break the egg and mix in a small bowl. Mix the almond meal (or other ground nut), salt and pepper (and other spices/herbs if desired) in another small bowl.

Place the cut tomato in the egg mixture, then in the almond mixture until well coated. Place in hot oil and fry until golden brown. Enjoy!

Makes 4 servings.
NUTRITIONAL COMPARISON (per serving):

Traditional Fried Tomatoes =
200 calories, 15g fat, 3g protein, 14g carbs, 1g fiber (13g effective carbs)

"Healthified" Tomatoes =
204 calories, 20g fat, 4.3g protein, 4.4g carbs, 2g fiber (2.2g effective carbs)

Garden Fresh Tomatoes...

When you just can't wait to eat that fresh garden produce,
pick a soft green tomato before it ripens for a flavorful entree.

Chicken and Salmon Patties

Ingredients:

16 oz. chicken breast, cut into chunks
    OR canned salmon
2 TBS coconut flour
1/4 c. finely chopped mushrooms
1/4 c. Parmesan cheese, grated
1/4 c. chopped green onions
2 tsp Cajun seasoning
1/4 tsp Celtic sea salt
1 egg
2 tsp coconut oil OR ghee

FOR THE AIOLI:
2 TBS organic mayonnaise
2 tsp prepared horseradish
1 tsp minced garlic
1/8 tsp salt

Directions...

If using chicken, add it to the food processor and pulse just until ground. Be careful not to pulse too long. In a medium bowl, mix together ground salmon or chicken, parmesan, chives, Cajun seasoning, 1/4 tsp salt, egg, coconut flour and mushroom pieces. Evenly divide mixture into 8 portions and flatten out into thick patties. Add oil in a large nonstick skillet over medium heat. Carefully place the patties in the pan and cook 6-8 minutes on each side or until done.

FOR THE AIOLI: In a small bowl, whisk together mayonnaise, horseradish, garlic and salt. Serve with the patties. This makes a small amount, so if you like things more saucy, I would double the aioli ingredients.

Makes 4 servings.
NUTRITIONAL COMPARISON (per serving)
Traditional Patties =
359 calories, 21g fat, 21g protein, 9g carbs, 0.5g fiber (8.5g effective carbs)

"Healthified" Chicken Patties =
268 calories, 9.6g fat, 39.7g protein, 2.9g carbs, 1.4g fiber (1.5g effective carbs)

"Healthified" Salmon Patties =
314 calories, 19g fat, 30g protein, 2.9g carbs, 1.4g fiber (1.5g effective carbs)

Our tongue has long been subdivided into four separate areas and tastes – sweet, salty, sour and bitter. Scientists now find that we have receptors unique to spicy flavors and fat. This fifth taste sensation is called Umami. Umami is best described savory, and is detected in amino acid rich foods that give a sense of lingering mouth-feel and body. Adding 1 tsp to foods like salad dressing provides a special taste that your guests will be wondering what makes your food so tasty! I add this to my meatloaf, sauces and marinades.

Crab Cakes

Ingredients:

1 pound crab meat
2 TBS diced green bell pepper
1 TBS Spectrum organic mayonnaise
3 TBS finely grated Parmesan cheese
   (or nutritional yeast if dairy allergy)
2 eggs
1 TBS aluminum free baking powder
2 tsp seafood seasoning
1 tsp fish sauce
   (Optional: umami flavor)
2 TBS expeller pressed safflower
   or coconut oil

EGGS:
4 eggs

GREENS:
1 TBS coconut oil or butter
14 oz. fresh spinach
1 tsp Celtic sea salt
1/2 tsp freshly ground black pepper
1/4 tsp nutmeg

Directions...

CRAB CAKES: In a medium-large bowl, mix all ingredients except oil until blended. Heat oil in a large skillet over medium-high heat. With a spoon, place 2 TBS of the crab mixture into the pan for mini-cakes. Cook until golden brown, about 2 minutes, and then flip and cook another minute.

EGGS: Heat pan to medium high heat. Place 1/4 cup water in the pan. Crack in the egg, cover the pan so it traps any air. Cook the egg just until the white are cooked, but the yolk is still soft and runny.

GREENS: Heat the coconut oil or butter in a frying pan over a low to medium heat. When it has melted, add the spinach and cook for 1-2 minutes, stirring constantly, until wilted. Add the spices to desired taste. Spoon the cooked greens into the center of a plate. Place 2-3 crab cakes on top of each portion, and top with an egg. Then watch the yolk pour all over the delicious crab cake as you break it open with a fork!

Makes 4 servings. NUTRITIONAL COMPARISON (per serving)
Traditional Crab Cake =
368 calories, 18g fat, 11g protein, 10g carbs, 0.8 g fiber (9.2g effective carbs)
"Healthified" Crab Cake =
248 calories, 10g fat, 13g protein, 0.4g carbs, trace fiber (0.4g effective carbs)

POACHING EGGS TIP

"Always acidulate the poaching liquid with either vinegar or lemon juice (1 tsp per each cup of water) to stabilize the whites. My tip is to crack the egg into a ramekin and soak the egg in a TBS of vinegar for 5 minutes. This helps the white from spreading so much in the water." Vinegar, or even lemon, helps the egg whites to set more quickly and we get fewer wispy bits when you add a tablespoon or two to the simmering water. I also suggest swirling the water very fast before dropping the egg in so the water naturally rolls over the egg to keep the whites from spreading. When poaching at a gentle simmer, four minutes gives us an egg with firm whites and a runny yolk. Four and a half minutes is perfect if we want a yolk that's just starting to set. Five whole minutes works for the times if you desire a yolk that is set yet still custardy and soft.

GARLIC HUMMUS (pictured above) tastes so good with fresh veggies.

CINNAMON SUGAR "HUMMUS" (pictured on the right) is a fun addition to my healthified bagel chips.
(see page 42, The Art of Healthy Eating - Kids for bagel chips recipe)

"HUMMUS"

Ingredients:

GARLIC HUMMUS:
1 large zucchini, cut into chunks
1/2 c. tahini
1 clove garlic, peeled
1 TBS macadamia nut or olive oil
2 TBS lemon juice
1 tsp cumin
1 tsp smoked paprika
1 tsp Celtic sea salt

CINNAMON SUGAR "HUMMUS"
Omit the garlic, cumin, and paprika.
Add 1/4 cup Swerve (or 1 tsp stevia glycerite)
2 tsp cinnamon.

Directions...

Combine all the ingredients in a high-powered blender or food processor and process until smooth. Taste and adjust the seasonings to taste. Serve with BAGEL CHIPS or FRESH VEGGIES.

Makes 4 servings.
NUTRITIONAL COMPARISON (per cup)
Traditional Hummus =
435 calories, 21g fat, 10g protein, 49.9g carbs, 9g fiber (40.9g effective carbs)
"Healthified" Hummus =
228 calories, 19g fat, 6.5g protein, 10.5g carbs, 3.9g fiber (6.6g effective carbs)

FAT BURNING TIP

Adding a few tsp of LEMON to each meal helps lower the insulin response to carbohydrates and slows the time it takes a meal to leave your stomach, which helps with weight loss and digestion.

Re-fried "Beans"

Ingredients:

1 eggplant - about 4 c. cubed (or zucchini)
1 bay leaf
4 slices bacon
1 c. chopped yellow onions
1 TBS minced garlic
1 TBS minced, seeded jalapeno
1 TBS chili powder
1 tsp ground cumin
1/2 tsp Celtic sea salt
 Pinch cayenne
1/2 tsp chopped oregano
1/2 c. grated queso blanco or
    cheddar cheese (optional)
1/4 c. minced fresh cilantro, garnish (optional)

Directions...

Peel and cube the eggplant. Place cubes and 4 slices of uncooked bacon pieces in a pan. Stir fry until bacon is fried and eggplant is very soft; about 10 minutes. Reserve bacon fat. Vegetarian OPTION: Peel and slice the eggplant, place in tinfoil and smoke in a wood smoker for 2 hours. This gives the eggplant a natural bacon flavor.

Place the eggplant (and bacon) in a food processor and puree until smooth. In a large, heavy skillet, heat the bacon fat over medium-high heat. Add the onions and cook, stirring, until soft, about 3 minutes. Add the garlic, jalapeno, chili powder, cumin, salt, and cayenne, and cook, stirring, until fragrant, 45 seconds to 1 minute. Add the eggplant puree and any cooking liquid from the pot, and the oregano, and stir to combine. Cook, stirring with a heavy wooden spoon, until the mixture forms a thick paste, 5 to 10 minutes, adding water 1 tablespoon at a time to keep from getting dry. Sprinkle with the cheese and cilantro, and serve. Use my "Healthified" tortillas for burritos!

Makes 8 servings. NUTRITIONAL COMPARISON (per serving)
Traditional Re-fried Beans = 183 calories, 6.6g fat, 7g protein, 24g carbs, 6g fiber (18g effective carbs)
"Healthified" Re-fried "Beans" = 93 calories, 5.6g fat, 5.7g protein, 5.8g carbs, 2.6g fiber (3.2g effective carbs)

Oregano
FUN HERB FACT

this super herb is very rich in anti-oxidant phytochemical flavonoids and phenolic acids. Oregano oil has been used as a disinfectant, an aid for ear, nose, & throat/respiratory infections, candida, and any sort of bacterial or viral conditions.

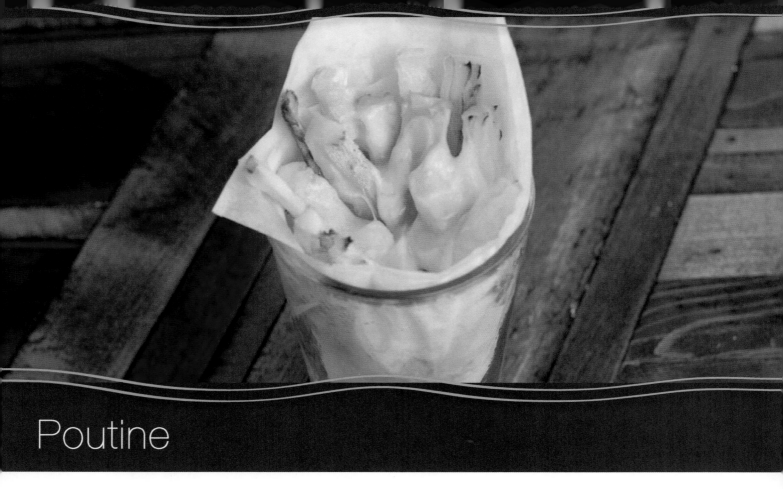

Poutine

Ingredients:

1 TBS coconut oil or butter
8 oz mushrooms, sliced
1 pound cauliflower
1 c. gravy
1 c. cheese curds

GRAVY:
2 TBS butter
1/4 to 1/2 tsp psyllium powder or
    guar gum (thickener)
2 c. organic beef broth
1 tsp organic Tamari soy sauce
1/4 tsp Celtic sea salt
1/4 tsp freshly ground pepper

Directions...

Melt the butter in a pan. Add the mushrooms and sauté until just starting to caramelize, about 10-15 minutes.

FRIES: Preheat the oven to 425 degrees F. Cut the stem out of the cauliflower (you can also use the whole cauliflower if you want, but it won't resemble "french fries"). Cut the stem into french fry shapes. Place on a greased cookie sheet. Spray the 'fries' with coconut oil spray and sprinkle with chili powder and salt. Bake for 25 minutes or until golden brown. Remove from oven, place on a large plate and mix in the mushrooms.

GRAVY: To make the gravy, mix in sauce pan for 10 minutes until thick and bubbly. Add more psyllium to desired consistency. Spoon gravy over fries and top with cheese curds. Enjoy!

Nutritional Comparison (per serving):
Traditional Poutine =
241 calories, 13.9g fat, 9.3g protein, 20.5g carbs, 2.5g fiber (18g effective carbs)
"Healthified" Poutine =
204 calories, 13.8g fat, 9.5g protein, 12g carbs, 2.6g fiber (9.4g effective carbs)

What's for dinner?

Something healthy that is sure to be a favorite.
Even your kids can't say no to this savory treat.

Farmer's Market Pie

Ingredients:

CRUST:
3 c. blanched almond flour
1/2 tsp Celtic sea salt
4 TBS of butter, cold and
   cut into small pieces
1 egg

FILLING:
1/3 c. stone ground mustard
4 medium tomatoes, sliced
1/4 tsp Celtic sea salt
1/8 tsp fresh ground black pepper
4 oz. crumbled Chevre (goat cheese)
1/4 c. chopped fresh herbs
   (parsley, rosemary, basil, marjoram, thyme)

Directions...
Preheat oven to 325 degrees F. In a medium sized bowl, mix together almond flour, salt, butter and egg. Press pie crust into pie dish or tart pan. Bake the crust for 12-15 minutes, or until it starts to lightly brown.

Remove from oven and spread the mustard in an even layer over the browned pastry, leaving 1/2-inch of the edges empty. Arrange the tomato slices over the mustard. Sprinkle the tomato slices with the sea salt, pepper, goat cheese and herbs. Serve the tart at room temperature or chilled.

Makes 12 servings.
Nutritional Comparison (per serving):

Traditional Pie =
334 calories, 21g fat, 9g protein, 27g carbs, 1.5g fiber (25.5g effective carbs)

"Healthified" Pie =
264 calories, 21g fat, 10g protein, 8g carbs, 3.8g fiber (4.2g effective carbs)

Farmer's Market Family Fun...

Do you love visiting the Farmer's Market?

If you have never been to one, you MUST go. You will be hooked.

Spinach Artichoke Tart

Ingredients:

CRUST:
1 1/2 c. of almond flour
1 1/2 c. of Parmesan cheese (grated)
1/4 tsp Celtic sea salt
1 clove garlic (optional)
1 egg

FILLING:
1 (10 oz.) package frozen chopped organic spinach, thawed and drained
1 ½ c. artichoke hearts, drained and chopped
1/8 tsp Celtic sea salt
1 clove garlic, minced
3/4 c. Parmesan Cheese
8 oz. macarpone or cream cheese softened
2 eggs

Directions... Preheat the oven to 325 degrees F. For the tart shell, combine the flour, cheese, salt and garlic and mix well. Add the egg and mix until the dough is well combined and stiff. Press pie crust into pie dish or tart pan. Bake the crust for 12-15 minutes, or until it starts to lightly brown.

Meanwhile, combine spinach, artichokes, salt, garlic, Parmesan Cheese, mascarpone and eggs. Pour mixture into prebaked tart shell. Sprinkle with extra Parmesan. Bake at for 30 minutes.

Makes 12 servings. NUTRITIONAL COMPARISON (per serving)
Traditional Tart = 270 calories, 18g fat, 10g protein, 16g carbs, 1g fiber (15g effective carbs)
"Healthified" Tart = 252 calories, 18g fat, 14g protein, 5.6g carbs, 2.2g fiber (3.4g effective carbs)

Crab Rangoon Torte

Ingredients:

CRUST:
1 1/2 c. of almond flour
1 1/2 c. of Parmesan cheese (grated)
1/4 tsp Celtic sea salt
1 egg

FILLING:
1/4 c. chopped scallions
1 TBS grated ginger
1 tsp Tamari sauce (soy sauce)
1 (8 oz.) package cream cheese, softened
2 eggs
2 TBS lime juice
1/2 tsp Celtic sea salt
12 oz. lump crab meat

Directions... Preheat the oven to 325 degrees F. For the tart shell, combine the flour, cheese, salt and garlic and mix well. Add the egg and mix until the dough is well combined and stiff. Press pie crust into pie dish or tart pan. Bake the crust for 12-15 minutes, or until it starts to lightly brown.

Meanwhile, combine all the filling ingredients. Pour mixture into prebaked tart shell. Sprinkle with extra Parmesan. Cook at 350 degrees F for 30 minutes.

Makes 12 servings. NUTRITIONAL COMPARISON (per serving)
Traditional Torte = 236 calories, 17.9g fat, 7g protein, 25.5g carbs, 1g fiber (24g effective carbs)
"Healthified" Torte = 222 calories, 17.9g fat, 11g protein, 4.8g carbs, 1.6g fiber (3.2g effective carbs)

Ginger
FUN HERB FACT

Ginger is excellent for treating upset stomachs and is still recommended to pregnant women today as a way to combat morning sickness. Ginger is also effective at treating gas and bloating, sore throats and colds. It is also anti-inflammatory and aids in digestion.

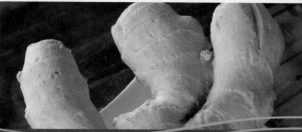

Chili Cheese Fries

Ingredients:

CHILI:
2 pounds grass fed ground beef
1 pound Italian sausage
2 (28 oz.) cans diced tomatoes
1 (6 oz.) can tomato paste
1 large yellow onion, chopped
3 stalks celery, chopped
1 green bell pepper chopped
1 red bell pepper chopped
2 green chilies chopped
4 pieces bacon (fried, drained and chopped)
1 c. beef broth
¼ c. chili powder
1 TBS minced garlic
1 TBS dried oregano
2 tsp ground cumin
1 tsp dried basil
1 tsp Celtic salt, pepper and paprika
1 tsp cayenne pepper
1 tsp stevia glycerite

FRIES:
2 heads of cauliflower stems
1 tsp Celtic sea salt
1 tsp chili powder

CHEESE SAUCE:
1/4 c. butter
3 TBS Cream Cheese
1/4 c. beef/chicken broth
1 c. sharp cheddar cheese, shredded
1/4 c. Parmesan cheese, shredded
Sea salt and pepper (to taste)

Directions...

CHILI: Heat a large stock pot over medium-high heat. Crumble the ground chuck and sausage into the hot pan, and cook until evenly browned. Drain off excess grease. Pour in the diced tomatoes and tomato paste. Add the onion, celery, green and red bell peppers, chili peppers, bacon, and beef broth. Season with chili powder, garlic, oregano, cumin, basil, salt, pepper, cayenne, paprika, and stevia. Stir to blend, then cover and simmer over low heat for at least 2 hours, stirring occasionally. After 2 hours, taste, and adjust salt, pepper, and chili powder if necessary. The longer the chili simmers, the better it will taste. Remove from heat and serve, or refrigerate, and serve the next day.
Makes 12 servings.

FRIES: Preheat the oven to 425 degrees F. Cut the stem out of the cauliflower (you can also use the whole cauliflower if you want, but it won't resemble "french fries"). Cut the stem into french fry shapes. Place on a greased cookie sheet. Spray the 'fries' with coconut oil spray and sprinkle with chili powder and salt. Bake for 25 minutes or until golden brown. Remove from oven. Spoon chili over fries and top with cheese.

SAUCE: In a saucepan, melt butter over medium heat. Stir in cream cheese and broth. Cook and stir for 2 minutes or until thickened. Reduce heat. Add the cheeses, stirring until melted. Add salt and pepper to taste. Remove from heat, pour over the veggie, and stir to combine. Top with the additional 1/2 cup cheese and bake until browned and bubbly hot, about 15 minutes.

Makes 12 servings. NUTRITIONAL COMPARISON (per serving)
Smashburger Chili Fries =
700 calories, 36g fat, 16g protein, 78g carbs, 7g fiber (71g effective carbs)
"Healthified" Chili Fries =
460 calories, 30.3g fat, 32.3g protein, 15g carbs, 5g fiber (10g effective carbs)

Baked Brie

Ingredients:

PASTRY:
1 1/4 c. blanched almond flour
    (or 3/4 c. coconut flour)
5 TBS psyllium husk powder
    (no substitutes)
2 tsp baking powder
1 tsp Celtic sea salt
2 egg whites (8 egg whites
    if using coconut flour)
1 1/4 c. BOILING water

FILLING and TOPPING:
1 (8 oz. size) wheel Brie
1/4 c. butter
3 TBS Nature's Hollow Xylitol
    honey (no substitutes)
2 TBS pecans

Directions...
Preheat the oven to 350 degrees F. In a medium sized bowl, stir together the almond or coconut flour, psyllium husks, baking powder and salt. Add the eggs. Stir continuously as you add the hot water. Combine until very smooth. Place the dough onto a piece of greased parchment paper. Using a rolling pin, roll the dough out in a circle shape with even thickness throughout. Place brie in center, and fold pastry around it, sealing seams. Transfer to baking sheet, seam side down. Bake brie until pastry is golden, 23-35 minutes. Drizzle with Nature's Hollow Honey. Sprinkle with pecans. Serve with "healthified" "Cheese It crackers (recipe on page 75 in The Art of Healthy Eating - Kids).

Makes 8 servings.
NUTRITIONAL COMPARISON (per serving)

Traditional Baked Brie =
401 calories, 30g fat, 9g protein, 27g carbs, 1.2g fiber (25.8g effective carbs)

"Healthified" Almond Flour Baked Brie =
208 calories, 15g fat, 10g protein, 7.7g carbs, 4.9g fiber (2.8g effective carbs)

"Healthified" Coconut Flour Baked Brie =
243 calories, 16g fat, 10g protein, 10g carbs, 7.5g fiber (2.5g effective carbs)

FYI:
The honey bear is the only animal found in nature with tooth-decay problems (honey decays teeth faster than table sugar). Honey = highest calorie content of all sugars with 65 calories/TBS, compared to the 48 calories/TBS found in table sugar. Make sure to use Nature's Hollow Honey to save lots of sugar and carbohydrates which will keep your children's blood sugar and mood stable.

Xylitol occurs naturally in many fruits and vegetables and is even produced by the human

Chicken Broccoli Braid

Ingredients:

2 c. diced, cooked chicken meat
1 c. fresh broccoli, chopped
1/2 c. red bell pepper, chopped
1 clove crushed garlic
1 c. shredded white Cheddar cheese
1/2 c. organic mayo
2 tsp dried dill weed
1/4 tsp Celtic sea salt
2 TBS slivered almonds
1/4 c. diced onion
BRAID:
3/4 c. coconut flour
2 TBS psyllium husk powder
1/4 tsp Celtic sea salt
1/4 c. butter OR
     coconut oil, softened
1 1/2 c. boiling water
1 egg white, beaten

Directions...

Preheat oven to 375 degrees F. In a large bowl, mix together chicken, broccoli, red bell pepper, garlic, Cheddar cheese, mayonnaise, dill weed, salt, almonds and onion. Set aside.

In a medium-sized bowl, stir together the coconut flour, psyllium husks, salt and spices. Add the butter or coconut oil. Stir continuously as you add the hot broth or water, it will melt the butter or oil. Combine until very smooth. Place the dough onto a piece of greased parchment paper. Using a rolling pin, roll the dough out in a rectangle shape with even thickness throughout. Using a knife or scissors, cut 1 inch wide strips in towards the center, starting on the long sides. There should be a solid strip about 3 inches wide down the center, with the cut strips forming a fringe down each side. Spread the chicken mixture along the center strip. Fold the side strips over chicken mixture, alternating strips from each side. Pinch or twist to seal. NOTE: Once you add the boiling water the dough will begin to cook so move quickly! Brush braided dough with the egg white. Bake in the preheated oven 25 to 28 minutes, or until golden brown.

NUTRITIONAL COMPARISON (per serving)
"PAMPERED CHEF" Broccoli Braid =
247 calories, 13g fat, 12.5g protein, 17g carbs, trace fiber (17g effective carbs) AND TRANS FAT!
"Healthified" Broccoli Braid =
229 calories, 13g fat, 12.5g protein, 13.7g carbs, 7.2g fiber (6.5g effective carbs)

Cancer Facts

Why are the rates of cancer going up? In 1840 the average American consumed 2 tsp of sugar a day...in 2011, a typical American consumes over 63 tsp of sugar PER DAY! Cancer LOVES glucose! This is why we test cancer patients by having them drink a "glucose" mix and watch where the cancer attacks. So you think, "Sure, just cut out the glucose from our diet." BUT most people don't understand where all the glucose is coming from. It isn't just the sugar. "Complex carbohydrates" are structurally just glucose molecules hooked together in long chains. The digestive track breaks it down into glucose. So a sugary and a starchy diet are pretty much the same thing. So in essence a bowl of oatmeal, skim milk and a banana is just a huge bowl of sugar.

For about 5 years now, German doctors have been testing cancer patients in a clinical study of a surprising prescription...fat. Their patients are on a ketogenic diet, which eliminates almost all carbohydrates and sugar, and provides energy only from high-quality fats. You are thinking..."this sounds completely opposite of the 'raw food' juicing cancer diets I have been reading about!" BUT this scientific evidence dates back more than 80 years. In 1924, Nobel Prize winner Otto Warburg published his observations of a common feature he saw in fast-growing tumors: unlike healthy cells that can get energy by metabolizing sugar in the mitochondria, cancer cells appeared to fuel themselves only through glycolysis, a less-efficient means of creating energy through the fermentation of sugar in the cytoplasm. Warburg believed that this metabolic switch was the primary cause of cancer, a theory that he was unable to prove before his death. If most aggressive cancers rely on the fermentation of sugar for growing and dividing, then take away the sugar and the cancer can stop spreading. Meanwhile, normal body and brain cells switch to generate energy from fatty molecules called ketones, the body's main source of energy on a fat-rich diet.

One theory that mistakenly sticks with cancer patients is that diet can influence our pH balance. Tumor cells release lactic acid as a by-product, and this became known as the alkalinity-acidity theory. This created a number of books that wrongly encouraged alkaline diets for preventing and curing cancer. In reality, cancer cells are a bit more acidic just outside their boundaries than inside due to the expelling of lactic acid. Trying to control the pH in your body appears to be bogus. Not only does the absence of acid in the gastric tract and bladder establish an environment that is favorable to tumor growth, the control of pH is automatically controlled in a neutral range of 7.2—7.4. Our diets have been proven to have no effect over the pH of the blood. I'm not saying to grab a bag of pork rinds and dip them in nacho cheese sauce. Quality food is essential! No trans-fat allowed! Consumer Reports even admitted that low-carb diets aren't bad like they once thought.

So enjoy these alongside of a large omega-3-filled grass-fed steak or filet of salmon!

Freezing Herbs
FUN HERB FACT

"In the middle of summer when herbs are fresh, organic and affordable at the farmer's market or your garden, here is a money saving tip: Chop herbs, fill an ice cube tray, drizzle with a quality olive oil or macadamia nut oil and freeze. Once frozen, store in an air tight ziplock bag. This way you can enjoy the wonderful tastes of summer all year long."

Steak Fries

Ingredients:

2 large portobello mushrooms
1 egg
1/4 c. almond meal*
1 tsp Celtic sea salt
Optional: additional spices

Directions...

Preheat oven to 350 degrees F. Cut the mushroom into long "french fry" shapes. In a medium bowl, scramble the egg. In another bowl, place the almond meal (*note: you could also use finely grated parmesan cheese for more flavor and lower carbs), salt and spices. Dip the mushroom fry into the egg wash, then roll in the almond flour mixture. Place on a greased baking sheet and bake for 15 minutes or until golden brown. Serve with low sugar ketchup. Yum!

Makes 2 servings
NUTRITIONAL COMPARISON (per serving)
BAKED French Fries = 155 calories, 5g fat, 2g protein, 29.1g carbs, 3.9g fiber (25.2g effective carbs)
"Healthified" Fries = 110 calories, 8.1g fat, 6.8g protein, 4.2g carbs, 1.9g fiber (2.3g effective carbs)

Hearty Fries

Made with a lot of love.

Serve with a Grass-Fed Beef Burger on a bed of lettuce. YUM.

Potted Crab

Ingredients:

1 lb crab meat
1 small dried chili
1/4 tsp fresh ground ginger
1 TBS lime juice, and 1 TBS zests of lime
1/2 c. coconut oil
1/2 tsp Celtic sea salt
Fresh basil leaves
1 loaf Protein Bread.
   see page 50. Make a loaf instead of puffs.

Directions...
Let the coconut oil soften to room temperature. If you are using fresh crab, boil the crab, and let it cool. Smash the chili in a mortar and add half the softened coconut oil, lime juice and lime zest. Then mix and smash everything together till you have a soft paste. Add the ginger and crab. Mix thoroughly and season with salt. Place the crab into cute serving dishes. Flatten the crab and smooth the surface with a spoon, then melt the remaining coconut oil and pour it on the crab, top the oil with fresh basil leaves. Cool in the fridge to set and leave it overnight for the flavors to meld. Serve with Protein Bread made into toast points by buttering the slices and toasting in a preheated oven at 375 degrees F for 7-10 minutes or until golden brown and slightly crispy.

Makes 8 servings.
NUTRITIONAL COMPARISON (per serving)

Traditional Potted Crab with Toast Points =
232 calories, 15g fat, 8g protein, 16.2g carbs, 0g fiber (16.2g effective carbs)

"Healthified" Potted Crab with Protein Points =
 212 calories, 15g fat, 13.1g protein, 1.2g carbs, 0g fiber (1.2g effective carbs)

Zucchini Prosciutto Ribbons

Ingredients:

DIP:
1/4 c. fresh lemon or lime juice
1/4 c. chopped mint
2 garlic cloves, very finely chopped
1 tsp finely grated lemon or lime zest
1 tsp ground turmeric
1/4 c. extra-virgin olive oil, plus more
   for brushing
1/2 tsp Celtic Sea Salt and freshly
   ground pepper

FOR SKEWERS:
4 medium zucchini, very thinly sliced
   lengthwise on a mandoline
6 oz. thinly sliced prosciutto

Directions...
Preheat grill. In a bowl, combine the citrus juice with the mint, garlic, lemon/lime zest, turmeric and the 1/4 cup of olive oil. Add salt and pepper to taste. Thread the zucchini and prosciutto onto 12-inch bamboo skewers. Lightly brush the zucchini and prosciutto with olive oil and season with salt and pepper. Grill the skewers over high heat until the zucchini and yellow squash are lightly charred, about 1 1/2 minutes per side. Serve with the mint dip on the side.

Makes 4 servings.
NUTRITION INFORMATION (per serving):
"Healthified" Salad = 221 calories, 16g fat, 11.7g protein, 9.5g carbs, 3g fiber (6.5g effective carbs)

Sloppy Joe Stuffed Peppers

Ingredients:

1 pound ground beef
2 TBS onion, chopped
1 stalk celery, chopped
1 clove garlic, minced
1/2 c. tomato sauce
1 drop stevia glycerite
   or sweetener to taste

1 1/2 tsp white vinegar
1/2 tsp mustard
1/2 tsp Celtic sea salt
1/8 tsp pepper
8 oz. cheddar cheese, shredded
3 green peppers, halved lengthwise

Directions...
Brown the ground beef, onion, celery and garlic; drain fat. Stir in all remaining ingredients except the cheese and green peppers. Simmer 10 minutes. Meanwhile, parboil the peppers in a little boiling water 3 minutes; drain. To shorten baking time, I cooked mine for almost 8 minutes. Place peppers in a baking dish. Stir half the cheese into the hamburger mixture; fill peppers with meat. Top with remaining cheese. Bake at 350 degrees F 15-20 minutes (5 -10 for me) until hot and bubbly and peppers are tender.

Makes 6 servings. NUTRITIONAL COMPARISON (per serving)
Traditional Sloppy Joes =422 calories, 19.2g fat, 36g protein, 24g carbs, 1.4g fiber (22.6g effective carbs)
"Healthified" Sloppy Joes = 314 calories, 17g fat, 34g protein, 5g carbs, 1.5g fiber (3.5g effective carbs)

Shrimp Stuffed Peppers

Ingredients:

3 whole bell peppers
1/4 c. coconut oil, (or butter)
12 medium shrimp - peeled,
   deveined and chopped
1/8 c. chopped fresh basil
2 cloves garlic, chopped

Celtic sea salt and pepper to taste
1/4 c. broth (chicken or other)
1/2 c. freshly grated Parmesan
cheese, divided

OPTIONAL:
Capers for garnish

Directions...
Preheat oven to 350 degrees F. Scoop out the flesh of the peppers; set aside. Heat 1/4 cup coconut oil or butter in a large, deep skillet over medium high heat. Sauté shrimp, basil and garlic until shrimp turns pink, about 1 minute. Season with salt and pepper. Pour in broth, and cook 5 minutes.

Transfer to a large bowl, and mix in 1/4 cup Parmesan cheese. Stuff mixture into pepper shells, and sprinkle top with remaining Parmesan cheese. Bake in preheated oven for 30 to 40 minutes, or until peppers are tender.

Makes 3 servings. NUTRITIONAL INFORMATION (per serving):
Shrimp Sandwich = 490 calories, 29g fat, 9g protein, 49g carbs, 1g fiber (48g effective carbs)
"Healthified" Shrimp = 235 calories, 23g fat, 9g protein, 9g carbs, 3g fiber (6g effective carbs)

Great Way to Use Leftovers!

Chicken salad is a fun way to use up your leftovers from a yummy chicken dinner like the one shown above. (see pg 73)

Smoked Chicken Salad

Ingredients:

4 c. cubed, smoked chicken meat
1 c. homemade OR
    organic mayonnaise
1 tsp paprika
1 green onion, chopped
1 c. chopped pecans
1 tsp Celtic sea salt
ground black pepper to taste

OPTIONAL:
Sliced hard boiled eggs
1 c. chopped celery
1/2 c. minced green pepper
8 Protein Buns

Directions...

Clean and breakdown chicken into thighs, breasts, wings. Place soaked wood chips in the bottom of your smoker, and place the chicken on the racks. Smoke (outside) for 3-4 hours depending on the manufacturer's directions. At this point you still want to finish cooking it in a pre heated oven at 250 degrees F for 30 minutes or until deep golden.

In a medium bowl, mix together mayonnaise with paprika and salt. Blend in onion and nuts (and other additions that you prefer: celery, or green pepper). Add chopped poultry, and mix well. Season with black pepper to taste. Add sliced hard boiled eggs if desired. Chill 1 hour. Use Protein Buns for sandwiches.

Makes 8 servings.
NUTRITIONAL INFO (per serving)

Traditional Sandwich =
445 calories, 23g fat, 27g protein, 30.5g carbs, 2.4g fiber (28.1g effective carbs)

"Healthified" Sandwich =
325 calories, 22g fat, 29g protein, 4g carbs, 1.5g fiber (2.5g effective carbs)

Quick Tip

Imitation Crab

A 2 cup serving of real crab meat is about 50 calories, 1 gram of fat, 7 grams of protein and less than 1 gram of carbohydrates. Imitation crab meat has about the same calorie and fat grams, but because the fake stuff is filled with sugars and starches, the carbohydrate content is very high for a so-called "protein" source. Some brands are 21 carbs and tons of undesired sugar per serving.

What exactly is imitation crab? The first issue is that it has 15 to 20 grams of carbs per serving! The last I checked crab didn't have any carbohydrates. So where do they come from? It starts with an overly processes white fish (Cod) and fortified with sugar, sugar, and more sugar. Cod is used primarily because it has a mild flavor that easily takes on the flavor of real crab meat, but also because it is cheap.

To create the "crab meat", they mince up the flesh of the fish, and suck out the water to make a thick paste known as surimi. Then they add starch (usually wheat or tapioca) to stiffen up the mixture. It wouldn't be our modern food supply without sugar...so they add that for a preservative so it can last forever in our fridge! Then they add egg whites to stabilize the "crab" which adds gloss and shine. Vegetable oils are also usually added to enhance the texture. If that weren't gross enough... to create the proper color and flavor, manufacturers add a variety of artificial flavorings; such as, carmine, caramel, paprika, and annatto extract – which also adds the pink color found in real crab meat. Monosodium glutamate (MSG) is also found in some brands to help enhance the flavor. Now, is that something you really want to eat? Also, do I have to go over what cocktail sauce is made from? The first ingredient is usually high fructose corn syrup. FYI: Some brands of imitation crab even glow in the dark!

CALORIES IN AND CALORIES OUT IS A LONG STANDING NUTRITIONAL MISCONCEPTION. The hormonal response in our body when we eat carbs/protein/fat is totally different. I am researching some studies and this one really stood out!

1000 calories at 90% fat = 0.9 lbs lost/day
1000 calories of 90% protein = 0.6 lbs/day
1000 calories of 90% carbs = weight GAIN of .24 lbs/day

Protein creates a 'thermic effect of food,' which means that when we consume protein some calories are 'lost' as heat. And healthy fats; such as coconut oil increases thermogenesis, which increases metabolism and produces energy. The medium chain fats in coconut oil goes directly to the liver and are immediately converted to energy, we call these KETONES. It also increases metabolism because it is easily absorbed and produces organelles in our cells. So my suggestion is to cut the carbs and sugar wherever possible and up the healthy fats!

Chicken Oscar with real crab. See page 75.

Ingredients:

PROTEIN BREAD:
6 eggs, separated
1 c. unflavored egg white or whey protein
1/2 tsp onion powder (optional)
4 oz. cream cheese or sour cream,
    room temperature

FILLING (per sandwich):
1 slice natural smoked bacon
4 oz. canned crab
1 TBS Spectrum Mayo
1 slice tomato
Handful of leafy greens

PROTEIN BREAD HINT:
Can add 1 tsp guar or xanthan
gum to the whipped whites to
help stabilize them.

Directions...
Preheat the oven to 375 degrees F. Separate the eggs (save the yolks for a different recipe... crème brûlée?), and whip the whites for a few minutes until VERY stiff. Slowly fold in the whey protein and onion powder if using. Then slowly fold in the cream cheese into the whites (making sure the whites don't fall). Grease a bread pan and fill with "dough." Bake for 40-45 minutes or until golden brown. Let completely cool before cutting or the bread will fall. Cut into 12 slices. I keep this bread in the freezer at all times to make sandwiches.

Makes 12 slices. NUTRITIONAL COMPARISON (per slice)

White Bread =
70 calories, 1g fat, 2g protein 14g carbs, 0.5g fiber (13.5g effective carbs)

"Healthified" Bread =
60 calories, 5.7g fat, 6g protein, trace carbs, 0g fiber (0g effective carbs)

NUTRITIONAL COMPARISON (per sandwich)

Traditional BLT =
343 calories, 12.5g fat, 31g protein, 26.6g carbs, 0.5g fiber (26.1g effective carbs)

"Healthified" BLT =
283 calories, 17.2g fat, 33g protein, 1g carbs, trace fiber (1g effective carbs)

Everyone was all up in arms when Dr. Oz featured a segment on arsenic in apple juice, but did you also know it is found in non-organic chicken? What is more concerning is the high levels of estrogen in chicken. Farmers have full knowledge that the estrogen will cause the animal to mature faster. Time magazine featured a ground breaking study of 17,000 girls at 8 years old. 15% of these girls are going through early puberty. This cover story cites that some chemicals mimic estrogen, and it is the increase in consumption of these chemicals responsible for the early puberty in children. What else are these estrogenic chemicals doing? Are you eating more fiber, taking the right probiotics, magnesium glycinate and still don't have bowel movements everyday? Has your doctor told you that it is fine and that is just how your body functions? Well, your doctor is wrong. Everyone should have bowel movements everyday...it is more important than you think. We are living in a sea of estrogens. When we aren't properly excreting those toxic levels of estrogens, they get stored in our fat cells which is responsible for weight. Fat cells make estrogen and estrogen causes fatty tissue growth. This is a vicious cycle we'd like to avoid. Excess estrogen is excreted in the bowel. When stool remains in the bowel for a longer time, as in constipation, the estrogen is reabsorbed.

Some ways we get too many estrogens is exposure to chemicals that mimic estrogen such as many plastics, microwaving food in plastic dishes, using plastic wraps and containers or eating non-organic food. Beef and chickens are typically given potent estrogenic substances ('super-estrogens') to make them more productive. Our produce is often laced with these substances. People develop estrogen dominance as a result of a high-carb low-fiber diet, consuming excess fructose, drinking alcohol, having a "Tired-Toxic Liver," or environmental factors...all of which we have some power to control.

The liver is a filter of sorts. It detoxifies our body, protecting us from the harmful effects of chemicals, elements in food, environmental toxins, and even natural products of our metabolism, including excess estrogen. Anything that impairs liver function or ties up the detoxifying function will result in excess estrogen levels. If your liver is tired and toxic, a special diet plan would be helpful. Estrogen is produced not only internally, but also produced in reaction to chemicals and other substances in our food. When it is not broken down adequately, higher levels of estrogen build up. This is true for both men and women, although the effects are more easily recognized in men. Alcoholic men with impaired liver function can develop a condition called gynecomastia, with estrogenic characteristics including enlarged breasts, loss of male pubic hair, and belly fat.

Some signs of excess estrogen in MEN and WOMEN:
-Migraines
-Low back pain
-Weight gain secondary to insulin resistance
-Belly fat accumulation (A "Beer Belly" is really an "Estrogen Belly")
-Fibrocystic breast disease
-Excessive PMS
-Menstrual disturbances such as irregular and heavy bleeding
-Endometriosis
-Fibroids
-Ovarian cysts
-Breast Cancer

Correcting Estrogen Dominance involves more than just correcting the estrogen-progesterone balance and supporting the adrenals. It is important to eliminate the factors as much as possible. Exposure to xenoestrogens, insufficient sleep, toxic exposure, poor nutrition (high carbohydrates, low fat/protein intake, low nutrient value), and stress are some common causes. I also have suggestions for supplements to help speed the process of healing. FYI: Even bar soaps leach estrogen's into our bloodstream.

So, do you feel like you are eating the right way, taking the right supplements and STILL aren't going #2?
It is most likely a food allergy!

Chicken and Waffles

Ingredients:

1 lb organic chicken breasts
1 c. almond flour
1 tsp Celtic sea salt
1/2 tsp parsley
1/2 tsp oregano
1/4 tsp pepper
2 eggs, beaten

8 PROTEIN WAFFLES:
1 c. almond flour or
   1/2 c. coconut flour
1 c. vanilla egg white or whey protein
1/2 tsp Celtic sea salt
1 TBS aluminum free baking powder
1 c. vanilla almond milk
   (1 1/2 c. if using coconut flour)
2 eggs (4 eggs if using coconut flour)
4 TBS butter or coconut oil, melted

Directions... Cut chicken breasts into thin strips, about one inch wide. Longer sections can be cut in half to have uniform pieces. Place almond flour, spices and salt in a shallow bowl. Dip chicken pieces into egg mixture, then dredge in almond flour mixture. Place on a greased baking sheet. Bake at 375 degrees F, for 10-12 minutes, until crispy on outside and lightly browned. Meanwhile, make the Protein Waffles. Preheat waffle iron to high. Combine the dry ingredients in a bowl. Combine the wet ingredients in another bowl. Slowly add the wet ingredients into the dry. Let sit for 5 minutes. Bake according to your waffle iron directions (I spray my waffle iron with coconut oil spray and bake a few minutes longer than a traditional waffle or it will stick). Once the chicken is finished, place on top of crispy waffles and serve with Nature's Hollow Syrup!

NUTRITIONAL COMPARISON (1 piece of chicken, 1 waffle and 1/4 cup syrup)
Traditional Chicken and Waffles = 619 calories, 19.3g fat, 40.4g protein, 72.1g carbs, 0.8g fiber (71.3g effective carbs)
"Healthified" Chicken and Waffles = 338 calories, 19g fat, 34.1g protein, 7.6 carbs, 3.2g fiber (4.4g effective carbs)

Creamy Chicken and Corn Bread Pancakes

Ingredients:

3 TBS butter or coconut oil
1/4 c. onion, chopped
2 chili peppers, seeded and diced
3 garlic cloves, minced
8 chicken breast, cut into bite-size pieces
1 tsp Celtic sea salt
1/2 tsp pepper
1 serving HOMEMADE cream of mushroom soup (see page 44)
8 oz. sour cream
8 oz. Cheddar cheese, shredded

PANCAKES:
4 eggs
1/4 c. coconut flour
1/4 tsp vanilla extract
1/4 c. unsweetened vanilla almond milk

Directions... Melt butter in a Dutch oven. Add onion, chile pepper, and garlic; sauté 5 minutes. Add chicken, salt, and pepper; cook, stirring often, 8 to 10 minutes or until chicken is done. Stir in the rest of the ingredients (except cheese) and stir until smooth. Add cheese, and cook 7 to 8 minutes or until cheese is melted. Serve over Corn bread Pancakes.

Mix the ingredients and let them sit for five minutes (or overnight). Oil or grease a pan and heat over medium heat. Pour about a 1/4 cup of batter for each pancake, brown on each side before flipping it.

Makes 8 servings. NUTRITIONAL COMPARISON(per serving):
Traditional Dish = 853 calories, 35g fat, 61g protein, 65g carbs, 4.9g fiber (60.1g effective carbs)
"Healthified" Dish = 597 calories, 29g fat, 65g protein, 10.5g carbs, 5g fiber (5.5g effective carbs)

Chicken Broccoli Bake

Ingredients:

FILLING:
1/2 c. butter or coconut oil
1 TBS coconut flour
1 tsp Celtic sea salt
Black pepper to taste
2 TBS finely chopped onion
2 c. chicken broth
4 slices bacon, chopped
1 1/2 c. sliced mushrooms
3 c. leftover chicken, chopped
2 stalks celery, finely chopped
1 c. broccoli, chopped

EASY "CRUST"
1 c. Jay Robb unflavored whey protein
4 TBS coconut oil OR butter, melted
    (plus extra for greasing)
2 c. unflavored almond milk
4 eggs
1/2 tsp Celtic sea salt

Directions...
Preheat the oven to 425 degree F. Grease pot pie dish with butter or coconut oil spray. In a medium sized bowl blend together the whey, almond milk, eggs and salt. Set aside.

In a large saucepan, melt 1/2 cup butter. Blend in coconut flour, salt, pepper and onion. Gradually stir in chicken broth. Cook, stirring constantly until smooth and thickened. In a separate pan, sauté chopped bacon and add mushrooms to sauté in bacon fat, then stir into saucepan. Stir in chicken, broccoli, celery. Mix well and pour into bottom of pie pan (or a soup cup, as featured in the above photo).

Place chicken mixture in the middle of the dish, packing tightly. Pour the whey mixture over the top of the chicken mixture until it just covers the chicken. Bake for 15 minutes at 425 degree F. Leave the oven closed and reduce heat to 325 degree F to bake for an additional 10-12 minutes.

Makes 8 servings.
NUTRITIONAL COMPARISON (per serving)

Traditional Pot Pie =
331 calories, 24g fat, 9g protein, 27g carbs, 1g fiber (26g effective carbs)

"Healthified" Pot Pie =
292 calories, 22g fat, 20g protein, 4.5g carbs, 1.2g fiber (3.3g effective carbs)

Buffalo Chicken with Blue Cheese Mash

Ingredients:

1 tsp coconut oil
Chicken Wings OR 1/2 lb
    chicken breasts - cut into strips
1/4 tsp Celtic sea salt
2 tsp butter
1 TBS hot pepper sauce

BLUE CHEESE MASH:
8 c. bite-size cauliflower florets
4 cloves garlic, crushed and peeled
1/2 c. blue cheese
1 tsp butter
1/2 tsp Celtic sea salt
Freshly ground pepper to taste

Directions...

Make Chicken: Heat oil in a large skillet. Season chicken with salt and sauté over medium high heat, stirring frequently, until lightly browned and cooked through, about 7 to 10 minutes. Remove skillet from heat. Add butter and hot pepper sauce to skillet and swirl until the butter melts and the sauce coats the chicken.

Place cauliflower florets and garlic in a steamer basket over boiling water, cover and steam until very tender, 12 to 15 minutes. Place the cooked cauliflower and garlic in a food processor. Add blue cheese, salt and pepper; pulse several times, then process until smooth and creamy. Transfer to a serving bowl. Serve with buffalo wings and enjoy!

NUTRITIONAL COMPARISON:

1 cup Potato "mashed" =
170 calories, 10g fat, 2g protein, 17g carbs, 1g fiber (16g effective carbs)

1 cup Cauliflower "mashed" =
28 calories, 0.5g fat, 1.8g protein, 5.2g carbs, 2.2g fiber (3g effective carbs)

Lemon Braised Chicken

Ingredients:

4 TBS coconut oil, divided
1 c. onion, minced
3 garlic cloves, peeled
4 chicken legs, drumsticks and thighs separated
1-2 tsp Celtic sea salt
1/2 c. flat-leaf parsley plus more for garnish
1/3 c. capers, drained
2 c. chicken broth
1/3 c. coconut or white wine vinegar (*see pg 31)
1 lemon, cut into thin strips
 Freshly ground black pepper

This is an awesome no-fail recipe that everyone needs in their cooking repertoire. A great thing about this recipe (besides the taste) is that you can halve, double or triple all of the ingredients based on your number of dinner guests. This dish is very forgiving, feel free to adjust the ingredients to your liking. I made it with fresh basil instead of parsley the second time around and it was excellent.

Directions...
Heat 2 TBS oil in a large heavy skillet over medium heat. Add onion and garlic; cook, stirring often, until softened, about 8 minutes. Transfer onion to a bowl; wipe skillet clean. Add 2 TBS oil to skillet and increase heat to medium-high. Season chicken with salt. Add chicken to skillet and cook, turning once, until golden brown on both sides, 10–12 minutes. Transfer chicken to a plate. Add reserved onion, 1/2 cup parsley, and capers to skillet; cook for 1 minute. Stir in broth and vinegar. Add chicken with any juices and the lemon slices. Reduce heat to medium-low; cover and simmer until meat is tender and falling off the bone, about 1 1/4 hours. Transfer chicken to a large platter. Season sauce in skillet with salt and pepper. Spoon over chicken; garnish with parsley.

Makes 8 servings. NUTRITIONAL COMPARISON (per serving)
Traditional Braised Chicken = 426 calories, 16g fat, 35g protein, 14g carbs, 1g fiber (13g effective carbs)
"Healthified" Braised Chicken = 304 calories, 16g fat, 35g protein, 2.7g carbs, 0.7g fiber (2g effective carbs)

Chicken Adobo

Ingredients:

4-5 lbs chicken thighs
1/2 c. coconut vinegar (see page 33)
1/2 c. coconut milk (or Tamari soy sauce)
4 cloves garlic, crushed
1 tsp black peppercorns
3 bay leaves
2 packages Miracle Rice or 4 c. riced cauliflower

There is some controversy about the use of Tamari (soy) sauce in the traditional dish, Chicken Adobo. This is a tasty Filipino dish; some believe that soy sauce was too much of a Chinese influence and therefore use coconut milk instead. That is how I made this recipe and personally, I prefer the taste this way!

Directions...
Combine the first six ingredients in a large pot. Cover and marinate chicken for 1-3 hours. Bring to boil, then lower heat. Cover and let simmer for 30 minutes, stirring occasionally. Uncover and simmer until sauce is reduced and thickened, and chicken is tender, about 20 more minutes. Serve with Miracle rice or sautéed cauliflower rice.

Makes 6 servings. NUTRITIONAL COMPARISON (per serving)
Traditional Adobo with rice = 506 calories, 16g fat, 47g protein, 40g carbs, 1.2g fiber (38.8g effective carbs)
"Healthified" Adobo = 337 calories, 16g fat, 44.4g protein, 2g carbs, 0.6g fiber (1.4g effective carbs)

A photo of the Crabmeat that I used is pictured above.

Chicken Oscar

Ingredients:

1 lb asparagus spears
4 boned skinless chicken
    breast halves
3-4 TBS coconut or
    blanched almond flour
1 tsp Celtic sea salt
1 sliced tomato (optional)
1/4 lb shelled cooked crab
    (I used wild caught crab
    from Sam's Club in jar)
1/2 to 2/3 c. hollandaise, warm
    (recipe follows)
Chive spears or minced chives

HOLLANDAISE:
4 egg yolks
1 TBS freshly squeezed lemon juice
1/2 c. unsalted butter, melted
1/4 tsp Celtic sea salt

Directions...

Preheat oven to 375 degrees F. Snap tough ends from asparagus; rinse. Rinse chicken, pat dry, wrap with plastic and pound down until 3/8 to 1/2 inch thick. Mix the coconut or almond flour and salt in a flat dish. Add chicken, turning and patting to coat. Place chicken breasts into a 9x13-inch baking dish. Bake chicken for 40 to 45 minutes or until it is no longer pink inside and juices run clear.

Meanwhile, make the hollandaise and cook asparagus. Whisk the egg yolks and lemon juice together in a stainless steel bowl and until the mixture is thickened and doubled in volume. Place the bowl over a saucepan containing barely simmering water (or use a double boiler,) the water should not touch the bottom of the bowl. Continue to whisk rapidly. Be careful not to let the eggs get too hot or they will scramble. Slowly drizzle in the melted butter and continue to whisk until the sauce is thickened and doubled in volume. Remove from heat, whisk in salt. Cover and place in a warm spot until ready to use.

In 10-12 inch frying pan over high heat, bring 1 inch water to boil. About 3 minutes before chicken is done add asparagus to boiling water. Cook until tender when pierced. Drain. Place sliced tomatoes and asparagus on warm plates. Top with chicken and crab. Pour hollandaise sauce over the top. Garnish with chives.

Makes 8 servings. NUTRITIONAL COMPARISON (per serving)

Traditional Chicken Oscar =
 526 calories, 22g fat, 76g protein, 7g carbs, 1g fiber (6g effective carbs)

"Healthified" Chicken Oscar =
 523 calories, 22g fat, 76g protein, 3.3g carbs, 1.5g fiber (1.8g effective carbs)

FUN FACT

Most people haven't heard of acetylcholine, but it is so important! Acetylcholine controls the brain's speed and mental process, keeping memory sharp and physical movements quick and precise. For most women are predisposed to an acetylcholine deficiency, because these symptoms set in with peri-menopause. Estrogen and testosterone stimulate the production of acetylcholine. As levels of those hormones decline, so does the production of this brain chemical. This prompts symptoms like memory lapses, dry skin and weight gain. To produce more acetylcholine enjoy egg yolks!

Chicken Parmesan is shown on the right. Eggplant Parmesan is pictured above.

Chicken and Eggplant Parmesan

Ingredients:

Tallow, Lard or Coconut Oil for frying
2 lbs boneless, skinless, chicken breasts
    OR 1 large eggplant
4 eggs whites
1/2 c. coconut flour (or almond flour)
1/3 c. finely grated Parmesan
    (or more flour instead)
1/2 tsp garlic powder
1 TBS finely chopped fresh basil
1/2 tsp Celtic sea salt
1 (24 oz.) jar marinara sauce
    (no sugar or soybean oil)

OPTIONAL TOPPINGS:
Parmesan
Mozzarella or Goat cheese
Basil leaves

Directions...

Heat 1 cup of lard, tallow or coconut oil in a large skillet or fryer on medium high. If using chicken breasts, butterfly and place into plastic wrap to pound with meat hammer until about 1/2 inch thick; if using eggplant, peel and slice into 1/2 inch thick round slices. Beat egg whites in a medium sized bowl until slightly frothy. *Egg whites are used for a crispier finished product, but whole eggs will also work fine in this recipe. On a large flat plate, combine coconut flour, spices and salt. Dip the chicken or eggplant into the frothy egg whites and then into the coconut flour mixture until well coated. Put directly into hot oil and cook, flipping once, until both sides have browned and chicken is cooked (about 4-5 minutes per side).

While the chicken or eggplant is cooking, heat sauce over medium heat until warmed. Place the sauce on a large-heat safe serving dish. Place the finished chicken or eggplant on top of the sauce. If using cheese, top the chicken or eggplant with the cheese and place in a broiler oven until cheese is melted. Serve alongside salad with my Super Salad Dressing!

Makes 8 servings.
NUTRITIONAL COMPARISON (per serving)

Traditional Chicken Parm =
457 calories, 24.2g fat, 39.7g protein, 19g carbs, 2g fiber (17g effective carbs)

"Healthified" Chicken Parm =
369 calories, 19g fat, 41g protein, 9g carbs, 4g fiber (5g effective carbs)

"Healthified" Eggplant Parm =
212 calories, 15.8g fat, 6.1g protein, 12g carbs, 6g fiber (6g effective carbs)

Beef Brisket

Ingredients:

1 1/2 c. paprika
3 TBS onion powder
3 TBS garlic salt
1 TBS celery salt
1 TBS black pepper
1 TBS lemon pepper
1 tsp mustard powder
1 tsp cayenne
1/2 tsp dried thyme
1 trimmed brisket,
    about 5 to 6 pounds

SERVE WITH...
Corn Bread (see page 19)
and coleslaw using
Super Salad Dressing (see page 31)

Directions...
In a bowl combine all the dry ingredients and blend well. Trim the brisket, leaving about 1/4-inch of fat. Season the brisket with about 1/4-cup of the rub. (If you don't want a thick crust of seasoning, let the brisket marinate overnight in the refrigerator and wipe off excess seasoning before placing in smoker). Preheat your smoker to 250 degrees F. Using indirect heat, smoke the brisket, fat side up, for 3 1/2 hours and flip. Cook another 3 1/2 hours, cooking for a total of 7 hours. (1 1/2 hours per pound.) (NOTE: You can also do this on a grill with the same temperature and time.) The brisket should cook to an internal temperature of 185 degrees F. Rest for 10 minutes on a cutting board before slicing. Slice brisket against the grain.

Makes 16 servings.
NUTRITIONAL COMPARISON (per serving)
Traditional Brisket = 380 calories, 11g fat, 49g protein, 20g carbs, 2g fiber (18g effective carbs)
"Healthified" Brisket = 331 calories, 11g fat, 49g protein, 4g carbs, 2g fiber (2g effective carbs)

FUN FACT

100g of apple has 7 mg of vitamin C and 100g of beef liver has 27mg!
Plus the fructose in the apple competes for the cellular absorption of vitamin C.
No sugar found in beef!

Chicken Cacciatore

Ingredients:

1 TBS coconut oil
8 small chicken thighs, skinless
1-2 tsp Celtic sea salt
1-2 tsp freshly ground pepper
3 c. baby portobello mushrooms, sliced
1 large sweet bell pepper, cut into strips
3 cloves garlic, minced
1/2 c. organic chicken broth
2 large tomatoes, cut into small chunks
1/4 c. onion, cut into thin slices
1 tsp oregano
2 TBS balsamic vinegar

OPTIONAL:
10 pitted Kalamata olives
capers
fresh basil leaves or rosemary

Directions...

Heat a large pan over medium heat with coconut oil. Season chicken with salt and pepper. Cook the chicken in the oil until browned on both sides. Remove chicken from pan and set aside.

Place the mushrooms, bell pepper and garlic into the pan and cook for 5 minutes. Add broth. Simmer until the liquid is almost evaporated. Add the diced tomatoes with their juices, onions, oregano; stir well to combine. Add the chicken back to the skillet, cover and simmer for about 20-23 minutes or until the chicken reaches 180 degrees F. Stir in balsamic vinegar. Season to taste with additional salt and pepper. If desired, top with olives, capers and fresh basil.

Makes 4 servings.
NUTRITIONAL COMPARISON (per serving)

Traditional Cacciatore =
780 calories, 54g fat, 31g protein, 35g carbs, 4g fiber (31g effective carbs)

"Healthified" Cacciatore =
317 calories, 9g fat, 31g protein, 9g carbs, 3g fiber (6g effective carbs)

Rosemary
FUN HERB FACT

Adding rosemary to your bone broth doubles the amount of calcium in the broth!

This recipe tastes wonderful with or without the bun.

Cheesesteak

Ingredients:

2 1/2 pound strip loin, trimmed
Coconut oil
Salt and freshly ground black pepper
Provolone Sauce, recipe follows
Sautéed Mushrooms, recipe follows
Caramelized Onions, recipe follows
Sautéed Peppers, recipe follows

PROVOLONE SAUCE:
1 TBS butter
1/2 c. chicken/beef broth
1 c. grated aged provolone cheese
4 oz. cream cheese
1 tsp Celtic sea salt
1/4 tsp freshly ground black pepper

SAUTEED MUSHROOMS:
2 TBS coconut oil
1 TBS butter
1 1/2 pounds mushrooms, sliced
3 TBS chopped fresh parsley leaves
Salt and freshly ground black pepper

CARAMELIZED ONIONS:
2 TBS unsalted butter
1 TBS coconut oil
2 large onions, peeled, halved and thinly sliced
1 tsp Celtic sea salt
1/4 tsp freshly ground black pepper

SAUTEED PEPPERS:
2 TBS coconut oil
2 poblano peppers, thinly sliced
2 Cubano peppers, thinly sliced
Salt and freshly ground black pepper

Directions...
Place steak in freezer for 30 to 45 minutes; this makes it easier to slice the meat. Remove the meat from the freezer and slice very thinly. Heat griddle or grill pan over high heat. Brush steak slices with oil and season with salt and pepper. Cook for 45 to 60 seconds per side. Place several slices of the meat on the bottom of 1/2 a Protein Bun (see page 50), spoon some of the cheese sauce over the meat, and top with the mushrooms, onions, and peppers.

PROVOLONE SAUCE: Melt butter in a medium saucepan over medium heat. Add in the rest of the ingredients and combine; season with the salt and pepper.

MUSHROOMS: Heat oil and butter in a large sauté pan over high heat. Add the mushrooms and cook until the mushrooms are golden brown. Stir in the parsley and season with salt and pepper.

ONIONS: Heat butter and oil in a large sauté pan over medium heat. Add the onions, season with salt and pepper, and cook slowly until golden brown and caramelized, stirring occasionally, approximately 30 to 40 minutes. Heat the oil in medium sauté pan over high heat. Add the peppers and cook until soft. Season with salt and pepper.

When done, you can use my Protein Buns recipe (see page 50) and cheese (mozzarella or provolone). But it tastes great without bread too!

Makes 8 servings.
NUTRITIONAL COMPARISON (per serving)

Traditional Philly =
571 calories, 19g fat, 53g protein, 48g carbs, 6g fiber (42g effective carbs)

"Healthified" Philly (without Protein Bun) =
351 calories, 17g fat, 43g protein, 4.2g carbs, 1.1g fiber (3.1g effective carbs)

"Healthified" Philly (with Protein Bun) =
397 calories, 20g fat, 65g protein, 4.8g carbs, 1.1g fiber (3.7g effective carbs)

Calcium Tip

Are you taking Tums in order to get your calcium? The active ingredient in Tums is calcium carbonate, which is also found in many calcium supplements. Calcium carbonate is the least absorbable form of calcium. Many people who suffer from kidney stones have too much calcium in their urine, a condition known as hypercalciuria. This can occur when taking poorly absorbed calcium supplements.

Southwestern Tabbouleh made with Miracle Rice. See page 114.

Acid Blockers

Are you or someone you know taking antacids on a daily basis? Antacids cause ulcers, chronic inflammation, leaky gut, food allergies, anemia, inflammatory bowel syndrome, restless leg, as well as other serious issues.

Your stomach is a very acidic environment, with a pH at 2 or less. Stomach acid is essential for the absorption of vitamin B-12 and minerals that allow you to release hormones from the pancreas, without which can lead to development of diabetes.

Stomach acid also helps break down protein. When you don't have stomach acid to break down food, undigested proteins sit like a rock in the intestines. This slowly eats holes in your intestines and this inflammation begins a detrimental snowball effect. When you start to have holes in your intestines, food starts to leak into your bloodstream (leading to leaky gut syndrome). This is awful because the immune system goes into overdrive to kill the unknown substances in the blood...NOW we have food allergies! So if you are a fan of cereal and skim milk, you will most likely have a wheat, corn and dairy allergy...oh boy! When this happens, other health issues follow; such as chronic/seasonal allergies, constipation and/or diarrhea and inflammatory bowel disease (IBS).

There are many natural ways to clear acid reflux without any side effects; such as aloe vera supplements. Aloe naturally repairs the damage that was done to the esophagus safely. aloe vera's major ingredient buffers pH+ and it naturally speeds the healing process. It is also important to eliminate foods that cause the problem: food chemicals, vegetable oils, sugar and starch. It could also be a food allergy/sensitivity; in this case eliminate gluten or the food causing the issue.

Eat foods that heal the intestines, like coconut oil, bone broth, and any "healthified" recipe that has no sugar. Adding supplements can heal the intestines faster so you can enjoy food again (Licorice Root, L-glutamine, Probiotics: Bifido and Acidophilius, Digestive Enzymes). Note: supplement dosages should only be made under the guidance of a professional.

Ingredients:

1/2 c. butter
1 TBS coconut flour
1 tsp Celtic sea salt
Black pepper to taste
2 TBS finely chopped onion
3 c. chicken broth
4 slices bacon, chopped
1 1/2 c. sliced mushrooms
3 c. cooked chicken, chopped
2 stalks celery, finely chopped
1 c. asparagus, chopped

CRUST RECIPE:
4 TBS coconut oil (or butter)
4 TBS coconut flour* (see NOTE)
2/3 c. almond flour

OPTIONAL:
2 TBS parmesan cheese
1 tsp Celtic sea salt

Directions...

Preheat oven to 400 degrees F. In a large saucepan, melt 1/2 cup butter. Blend in coconut flour, salt, pepper and onion. Gradually stir in chicken broth. Cook, stirring constantly until smooth and thickened. In a separate pan, sauté chopped bacon and add mushrooms to sauté in bacon fat, then stir into saucepan. Stir in chicken, asparagus, celery. Mix well and pour into bottom of pie pan or 8 soup dishes.

CRUST: In a medium bowl, mix all the ingredients until a thick dough forms (add Parmesan cheese for additional flavors). Place on a greased sheet of parchment, and cover with another piece of greased parchment. Using a rolling pin, roll out the dough into a 1/8th inch thin crust. Cover the pie pan/soup dishes with crust, seal edges, and cut away excess dough. Make a few small slits in the top to allow steam to escape. Bake in the preheated oven for 30 minutes, or until pastry is golden brown, and filling is bubbly.

NOTE: Not all coconut flours are created equal. Some brands have different baking properties. I always use Coconut Secret Raw Coconut Flour. You can find it here: http://astore.amazon.com/marisnutran05-20/detail/B003XB3NNE

Makes 8 servings.
NUTRITIONAL COMPARISON (per serving)

Traditional Pot Pie (with top and bottom crust) =
 623 calories, 42g fat, 19g protein, 42g carbs, 3g fiber (39g effective carbs)

"Healthified" Pot Pie =
356 calories, 26g fat, 22g protein, 6.3g carbs, 3.1g fiber (3.2g effective carbs)

Fibromyalgia and Chronic Fatigue

My heart goes out to all the people suffering from fibromyalgia and chronic fatigue syndrome. This is a debilitating disease that some doctors often dismiss. Yet I believe it is legitimate and stems from a variety of nutritional deficiencies.

INFLAMMATION: One of the reasons so many people are dealing with inflammation is due to a rapid rise in blood sugar, which causes biochemical changes in the cell. Choosing low carbohydrate foods is one of the best ways to decrease inflammation. When blood sugar rises, sugar attaches to collagen in a process called "glycosylation," increasing inflammation. Athletes also mistakenly eat too many carbohydrates, hindering their healing and recovery time because they are constantly causing joint inflammation.

SUGAR/GLUCOSE/FRUIT: Sugar dampens our immune system, which also increases fibro and chronic fatigue. The "phagocytic index" tells you how rapidly a particular lymphocyte can gobble up a virus, bacteria, or cancer cell. Glucose and vitamin C have similar chemical structures, so what happens when the sugar levels go up? They compete for one another when entering the cells. And the thing that mediates the entry of glucose into the cells is the same thing that mediates the entry of vitamin C into the cells. If there is more glucose around, there is going to be less vitamin C allowed into the cell. It doesn't take much: a blood sugar value of 120 reduces the phagocytic index by 75%. So when you eat sugar, think of your immune system slowing down to a crawl. Sugar is disguised in our foods as sucrose, polydextrose, corn syrup and maltodexterin. Even fruits and fruit juices contain a lot of sugar. Sugar also increases blood sugar which causes inflammation and pain.

HORMONES and LIVER FUNCTION: We get too much estrogen via exposure to chemicals that mimic estrogen, such as many plastics (microwaving food in plastic dishes or using plastic wraps and containers) or eating non-organic food. Beef and chickens are typically given potent estrogenic substances ('super-estrogens') to make them more productive. People develop estrogen dominance as a result of a high-carb, low-fiber diet; consuming excess fructose, drinking alcohol, having a "Tired-Toxic Liver" (see chapter in Secrets to a Healthy Metabolism), or environmental factors...all of which we have some power to control. The liver is a filter of sorts. It detoxifies our body, protecting us from the harmful effects of chemicals, elements in food, environmental toxins, and even natural products of our metabolism, including excess estrogen. Anything that impairs liver function or ties up the detoxifying function will result in excess estrogen levels. If your liver is tired and toxic, a special diet plan is needed to help. Estrofactors is a product by Metagenics that detoxes the liver from excess estrogen.

CANDIDA: An overgrowth of yeast can cause muscle and joint pain, difficulty concentrating, chronic fatigue, neurological disorders, insomnia, bowel dysfunction, and a weakened immune system. These symptoms are very similar to fibromyalgia. If you have been on antibiotics, have low moods, and you crave carbs and sugar, you could have an overgrowth of yeast. A low carb, low sugar diet along with the correct probiotics help to kill the yeast.

EXCITOTOXINS: Monosodium glutamate (MSG or Accent), aspartame (NutraSweet or Equal), hydrolyzed protein, are excitotoxins to our brain and should be eliminated by everyone. They are found in just about every existing boxed and packaged food out there. Excitotoxins excite the neurons in the brain, causing them to fire so rapidly that they die. Once these cells are dead, they can't be remade. A very scary reality is that when we eliminate these food additives, symptoms initially get worse as the body detoxifies.

PHOSPHATES: Most fibrous foods such as seeds, wheat, and oats have phytic acid. Many people with chronic fatigue and fibromyalgia have a genetic defect that prevents the kidneys from excreting phosphates. The phosphates build up in the bones, and eventually the muscles, ligaments and the tendons. The high phosphate level damages the cells' ability to produce ATP (energy) and causes the muscles to spasm. Coconut fiber does not contain phytic acid so it helps improve mineral status when you use it instead of wheat flour in your baked goods.

FREE RADICALS: An abundance of oxidative damage to the cells can cause fibro and chronic fatigue. Restoring the cells and eliminating free radicals is essential. Supplements are necessary for restoration.

MINERAL DEFICIENCIES: Magnesium is a miracle mineral, yet roughly 70% of people have a magnesium deficiency. Insulin stores magnesium, but if your insulin receptors are blunted and your cells grow resistant to insulin, you can't store magnesium so it passes out of your body through urination. Magnesium in your cells relaxes muscles. If your magnesium level is too low, your muscles will constrict rather than relax, which will increase pain and decrease your energy level. To fix this problem, eat a low carb diet and consume magnesium glycinate.

FOOD ALLERGIES: Having a food allergy, such as gluten, inhibits your intestines from absorbing iron and B-12; both are essential for energy production. When we inhale, we carry oxygen through the hemoglobin to the mitochondria of our cells that burn fat and create energy. If we are deficient in iron, we can't carry the oxygen to the mitochondria.

NIGHT SHADES: Another possible source of pain comes from the "nightshade plants." Vegetables such as potatoes, tomatoes, and eggplant contain a chemical alkaloid called solanine. Solanine can trigger pain in some people. If you are not sure, I suggest eliminating these foods for 1 month to see what happens.

OTHERS: Not getting REM sleep, imbalance of omega 3 to omega 6 ratio, a damaged immune system, parasites (which damage the immune system), and lack of exercise.

Light Italian Meatloaf

Ingredients:

1 1/2 lbs grass fed ground beef
1/2 lb Italian sausage
2 eggs, beaten
3/4 c. finely chopped mushrooms
1/2 c. grated Parmesan cheese
1/4 c. no sugar marinara
1 tsp Italian-style seasoning
1 tsp dried oregano
1 tsp dried basil
1 clove crushed garlic
1 1/2 c. shredded fontina or mozzarella cheese

Directions...
Preheat oven to 350 degrees F. In a large bowl, mix together ground beef, Italian sausage, eggs, mushrooms, Parmesan and marinara. Season with Italian-style seasoning, oregano, basil, garlic, and cheese. Press into a 9x5 inch loaf pan, and cover loosely with foil. Bake in the preheated oven approximately 1 hour, or until internal temperature reaches 160 degrees F.

Makes 6 servings
NUTRITIONAL COMPARISON (per serving)

Traditional Meatloaf =
535 calories, 33g fat, 29g protein, 16.2g carbs, 1.4g fiber, (14.8g effective carbs)

"Healthified" Meatloaf =
475 calories, 31.6g fat, 43.3g protein, 2.3g carbs, 0.5g fiber, (1.8g effective carbs)

SERVE WITH
"faux"tatoes (see page 73) and
"corn"bread (see page 19)
Pesto Rolls and Goat Cheese (see page 25)

HELPFUL HINT:

Instead of using bread crumbs or cracker crumbs, I use an egg for the binder along with finely chopped mushrooms (don't worry you don't even taste them, but it makes it very moist) and grated Parmesan cheese. Mushrooms and aged cheeses have something called "UMAMI." Umami is a pleasant savory taste produced by glutamate and ribonucleotides, chemicals which occur naturally in many foods. Umami is subtle and not generally identified by people when they encounter it, but blends well with other tastes to intensify and enhance flavors; it plays an important role in making food taste delicious.

When it comes to burgers, do you choose turkey or beef? Many people trying to eat a healthier diet opt for a turkey burger, believing it will be healthier for them. BUT are you often tired, have a hard time losing weight, have thinning hair? Before you place your next order, you may want to take a closer look at the two types of meat to see how they compare. You may be switching back to the beef!

Iron is necessary to make hemoglobin, the substance that carries oxygen through your blood to all the cells in your body. Hemoglobin is what makes red blood cells red. With insufficient iron, and therefore not enough hemoglobin, red blood cells become small and pale and don't carry enough oxygen. You may have heard the phrase "tired blood." This really means blood that is low in iron and that can't carry enough oxygen to vital organs and muscles. "Tired blood" results in a tired body. I often see clients that I would consider "workout warriors," but they never lose a stitch of weight. When we do a ferritin level test, they are often low in iron. This is problematic because in order to lose fat you must get the oxygen you inhale into the mitochondria of your cells where you burn fat. Iron is needed not only for blood, but also for brains. Neurotransmitters, the neurochemicals that carry messages from one nerve to another, require sufficient iron to function properly. A person with an iron deficiency may have a tired mind as well as a tired body.

To be fair, it really depends on what the beef AND the turkeys have been fed. In order to compare apples to apples, the nutritional value of extra lean ground beef (not more than four percent fat) and extra lean turkey meat is very close. While there are certainly differences between the two, it may shock some to see that the turkey burger and the hamburger vary only slightly across the board.

Now, let's check out grass-fed beef. It is much higher in vitamin E, and very rich in essential fatty acids like omega-3s and conjugated linoleic acid (CLA). CLA also helps convert fat to lean muscle mass. When taken in effective doses, CLA decreases body fat, especially in the area of the abdomen. Various studies prove the following additional benefits:
1. It can increase the rate of metabolism and is evidently very beneficial for thyroid patients.
2. People suffering from high triglycerides can use this to lower levels at a faster rate.
3. It can also increase the growth of muscles which we now know stimulates our metabolism.
4. Many people suffer from the serious issue of insulin resistance in which CLA can be used
to lower this resistance and therefore assist in controlling weight.
5. It can decrease Adrenal imbalances, which decreases abdominal fat stores.
6. It can help calm hormonal shifts; an area of concern to thyroid patients.
7. CLA has a very positive effect on our body by enhancing our immune system.

Many athletes and clients that want to lose weight spend loads of money on supplements containing CLA, but if they would just spend the extra money on quality beef, they could skip the supplements. CLA reduces fat but also preserves the muscle tissues. The most amazing part is not that it makes fat cell smaller, but it prevents a small cell from becoming fatter. A low calorie diet often helps a person lose weight for a short period, but once the cravings take over and the diet comes to a halt, that person is even more likely to gain back the weight. CLA seems to stop this undesired weight gain from happening because it causes you to hold onto valuable muscles during weight loss. Studies show that CLA is also helpful in lowering blood sugar levels. In one study almost 2/3 of the volunteers had a reduction of blood glucose level and triglyceride levels. SO, instead of spending money on supplements, let's buy QUALITY grass fed meat that is filled with CLA! (mushrooms and cheese are also high in CLA)

Let's go back to turkey...it doesn't have CLA...it does have arsenic, though. Since the 1960s, large-scale poultry producers have added arsenic to their poultry feed. Small amounts speed the growth of the birds, make their breast meat pinker, and kill certain bacteria. Chronic exposure to high levels of arsenic has been linked with cancer, heart disease, diabetes and a decline in brain function. But as long as poultry meat has fewer than 0.5 parts of arsenic per million, the USDA has declared that it is safe to eat.

Within the past few years, studies show that arsenic is a more potent cancer promoter than first believed. It has to do with its effect on blood vessels. The reason that arsenic makes white meat pinker is that it increases the growth of blood vessels in the meat. The more blood, the pinker the meat. That process is called "angiogenesis." It plays a major role in cancer promotion. Cancer cells can't speed up their growth without the creation of new blood vessels to fuel them with nutrients. Arsenic does the trick. The European Union banned the use of arsenic in poultry production in 1999. So with that said... I'm sticking to my grass fed beef! It tastes much better anyway.

EGGcelent Meatloaf

Ingredients:

4 eggs
1 onion, chopped
1 TBS butter
1 tsp Celtic sea salt
2 pounds grass fed ground beef
1 c. finely chopped mushrooms
1 c. freshly grated Parmesan cheese
20 slices nitrate free bacon

FUN FACT:

A traditional meatloaf calls for bread crumbs and onions which both have a lot of starch in them. So in my recipe, I decrease the onion in 1/2, and I swap the bread crumbs for 1/2 mushrooms and 1/2 Parmesan cheese. Mushrooms and Parmesan are known to have "umami." Umami is the Japanese word for savory. Using certain foods with Umami enhances flavor greatly!

Directions...

Preheat the oven to 400 degrees F. Bring a saucepan of water to a boil and then boil 3 of the eggs for 7 minutes. Rinse in cold water and set aside. Peel and chop the onions, and heat the butter in a thick-bottomed frying pan. Cook the onions gently sprinkled with the salt, for about 20 to 25 minutes or until the onions are golden. Remove to a bowl to cool. Put the raw egg, ground beef, chopped mushrooms and Parmesan cheese into a bowl, and when the onion mixture is not hot to the touch, add to the bowl and work everything together with your hands. Divide the mixture into 2, put half of the meatloaf into the bottom of a bread pan. Peel and place the 3 hard-boiled eggs in a row down the middle of the meatloaf (or you could make individual meatloafs in large muffin tins with one hardboiled egg in each meatloaf muffin).

Shape the remaining mound over the top of the eggs and pat into a solid loaf shape. Cover the meatloaf with slices of bacon, tucking the bacon ends underneath the meatloaf to avoid its curling up as it cooks.

Bake for 1 hour, until the juices run clear and once it's out of the oven let the meatloaf rest for 15 minutes. This recipe was inspired by Nigella Lawson.

NUTRITIONAL COMPARISON (per 4 ounce serving)
Traditional Meatloaf =
535 calories, 33g fat, 29g protein, 16.2g carbs, 1.4g fiber, (14.8g effective carbs)
"Healthified" Meatloaf =
528 calories, 33.6g fat, 49.7g protein, 3.3g carbs, trace fiber (3.3g effective carbs)

I get a lot of questions on how much fat is in my recipes. Why don't I label it? Well, because fat is my source of energy. I even run marathons with this diet and I never "hit the wall".

People often complain of low energy when they first start a low carb diet because they are "sugar-burners." This is not only inefficient, but very detrimental to our health. For one reason, cancer LOVES sugar! This is why cancer patients drink a huge glass of glucose to see where the caner is in their body. Cancer feeds on sugar, the more sugar you eat, the more the cancer grows.

Energy actually comes from a chemical we produce in our body called adenosine triphosphate (ATP). We can produce energy 2 ways: anaerobic and aerobic.
1. Anaerobic ('without oxygen') bacteria break down glucose to produce energy. Our cells can use this method.
2. Aerobic ('with oxygen'). All human and animal life requires oxygen to function.

As we breathe in oxygen, we carry it through the hemoglobin to the mitochondria (the powerhouse of our cells) where we burn fat and produce energy. The more mitochondria, the more energy and fat burning going on. AND the more healthy fats = more mitochondria. You can also increase the amount of mitochondria with certain supplements which I discuss in my book Secrets to a Healthy Metabolism. One supplement I take everyday for this is CoQ10.
*Please note that if you have a food allergy, you can't absorb iron properly which will inhibit you from carrying oxygen to the mitochondria. This will cause exhaustion due to low ATP production along with other problems.

Energy Can Come From:
1. Glucose: created with carbohydrates and protein
2. Fats, both from the diet and from stored body fats
3. Ketones which are derived from the metabolism of fats

GLUCOSE and ENERGY = EAT PROTEIN
Some cells, such as the kidneys, have very little mitochondria so they don't use fat for energy, so this is why eating protein for glucose is important. If we go too long without eating, we maintain glucose levels by breaking down glycogen in muscle proteins with a process called gluconeogenesis. BUT this is not healthy. There is a detrimental phenomena called SARCOPENIA where we lose 1% of our muscle every year starting at age 25, which is terrible because 1 pound of muscle burns 50 calories and 1 pound of fat burns only 2...even when we sleep! So we don't want to be cannibals to our muscles. Eating adequate amounts of protein will produce glucose (healthy carbs such as non-starchy veggies and almond/coconut flour will too). Our cells need a steady supply of protein to sustain a healthy structure. Any protein over and above 1 to 1.5 grams/kilogram of lean body weight/day can be used as a source of glucose. Anything less will cause you to start eating healthy muscle tissue. When you eat protein, you convert about 58% to glucose. So 100g of protein will produce 58 grams of glucose.

KETONES and ENERGY = EAT HEALTHY FATS
So if you want to stop being a "sugar burner" you must derive energy from another source. Enter fat. When we start eating a healthy low carb diet, our bodies slowly switch from burning sugar to burning fat. This is where eating becomes an "art." Energy must be derived from healthy fatty acids and ketones produced from foods such as coconut oil. At first the body will feel lethargic due to the mechanisms switching over; burning sugar is easy, burning fat takes a few days to adapt. The brain prefers to use ketones instead of glucose for energy (in Alzheimer's the brain can no longer convert glucose for energy; coconut oil is VERY healthy for these patients!).

Eating a very low carbohydrate diet stimulates the production of ketones from body fat; which is why people lose so much weight on this diet. Cutting out carbs and reducing protein also leads to a lower insulin level in the blood. A normal blood sugar is 1 TEASPOON of sugar in your blood. Many Americans consume over 63 teaspoons a day! If you can conquer a normal blood sugar, it reduces the problems associated with high insulin levels; insulin resistance, leptin resistance, high blood pressure, Metabolic Syndrome, weight gain, sleep issues...

Don't eat just lean proteins! It is not tolerated well in our body and leads to nausea in as little as three days. A high healthy-fat diet, however, is the traditional diet to sustain for a lifetime. Eating only lean protein causes excess intake of nitrogen, which leads to hyperammonaemia, which is a build up of ammonia in the bloodstream and is toxic to the brain. Many traditional societies survived on a purely animal product diet, which was naturally high in fat...they didn't have George Foreman grills.

Our paleo ancestors actually consumed more fat than protein; with a ratio of about 80% calories from fat and 20% from protein. During prolonged periods of starvation or something such as marathon running, fatty acids are converted into ketones, the preferred energy source for highly active tissues like those found in the heart and muscles. Ketones provide long lasting energy to all cells with mitochondria. Ketones are used to generate ATP. If you use glucose for energy, it needs the intervention of bacteria; ketones can be used directly.

*NOTE: Using a quality REAL salt is also essential for electrolyte balance. We start skipping the salt and we get low energy. I'm not talking about pre-packaged and fast food junk salt. A Celtic sea salt filled with minerals will help with energy.

The healthiest, more energizing fats come from animal sources. Quality animal sources like free-range egg yolks and grass fed beef!

Tomato Tart.
A variation of the Tomato Tart. (See page 57). Using different colors and types of tomatoes can really change the look.

Digestive Help

Digestive problems? Yeast infections? Chronic Fatigue? Allergies? IBS? Cravings? Eating fermented vegetables daily is a natural cure. If you have a history of using antibiotics, it causes your gut to be more susceptible to parasites and Candida overgrowth. A healthy large intestine is very acidic and has lots of beneficial bacteria such as Lactobacillus acidophilus. These healthy microorganisms feed on the waste left over from our digestion and create lactic acid. We need the lactic acid that they produce to keep our colons healthy and in an acidic state. Without them the colon does not have enough acidity to stop the growth of parasites and yeasts, and eventually the environment becomes hostile to acidophilus. Some of the signs of candida yeast overgrowth are: fatigue, poor memory, a "spacey" feeling, intense food cravings, gas, loss of sexual desire, bad breath and indigestion. Candida has also been directly linked to allergies, chronic fatigue syndrome, irritable bowel syndrome, multiple chemical sensitivity disorders and various cancers. Use of antibiotics, birth control pills, alcohol and refined foods all increase the risk of developing candida. These desired microorganisms that create lactic acid in the colon are naturally found in all vegetables and helps turn cabbage into highly-digestible sauerkraut. The fermentation process increases the amount of microorganisms. Lactic acid also helps digestion at an earlier stage in our stomach. As we get older, our stomach's natural secretions of hydrochloric acid decrease. Hydrochloric acid breaks down food so it can be more easily absorbed by the small intestine. It is also the most important defense we have against harmful bacteria and parasites often present in food. Lactic acid can help compensate for reduced hydrochloric acid.

Unpasteurized sauerkraut benefits digestion in the stomach by assisting the pancreas. The pancreas secretes essential digestive enzymes into the stomach. It is loaded with naturally occurring beneficial bacteria, digestive enzymes, lactic acid, sulphur and easily digested vitamins and minerals. Traditionally, sauerkraut is made with only two ingredients - Cabbage and salt. Spices may be added, too. However, pasteurization, vinegar, water and preservatives are short cuts to making good sauerkraut and are telltale signs of poor quality 'kraut. So if you buy it from a can, it is pasteurized and pasteurization will destroy all of the beneficial digestive enzymes and lactic acid bacteria, as well as the valuable vitamin C content, so it greatly diminishes the nutritional value without any significant benefit. So here is a recipe for our digestion!

Reuben Enchiladas

Ingredients:

1 large head of cabbage
8 oz. corned beef
8 oz. cream cheese
3 c. sauerkraut
2 c. Swiss cheese, shredded

Directions...
Preheat oven to 400 degrees F. In a pot, boil water and place large leaves of cabbage in the water. Boil for 5-7 minutes or until tender. Spray a baking pan with nonstick coconut oil spray and set aside. Place the corned beef in a bowl and shred using two forks; one to hold the beef in place and the other to scrape across the meat. Add cheese, sauerkraut, and cream cheese. Mix well and set aside. Lay cabbage tortillas out flat, and evenly distribute corned beef mixture in the center of cabbage. Wrap the cabbage tortillas up tightly, and place them in the baking pan with the seam sides down. Bake in the oven until hot, about 10 minutes.

Makes 6 servings. NUTRITIONAL COMPARISON (per serving):
Using Corn Tortilla = 447 calories, 31.5g fat, 22.1g protein, 20.2g carbs, 4g fiber (16.2g effective carbs)
Using Cabbage Tortilla = 377 calories, 30g fat, 22.7g protein, 6.2g carbs, 2.1g fiber (4.1g effective carbs)

Mexican Lasagna

Ingredients:

1 TBS coconut oil
2 skinless chicken breast
   cooked and shredded
   (I used a crock-pot)
*OR you could use 1 lb
   grass fed ground hamburger
1/2 c. chopped onion
1 (7 oz.) can chopped
   green chile peppers

2 TBS of taco seasoning
   (see page 90)
1/2 c. tomato sauce
2 eggs
2 c. cottage cheese
1 tsp Celtic sea salt
1/4 tsp freshly ground black pepper
10 "healthified" tortillas (see page 20)
2 c. shredded Monterrey Jack cheese
1 (10 oz.) can tomato sauce (or salsa)

Directions...
To make the meat mixture, heat oil in medium skillet over medium high heat. Add chicken or ground beef, onion and green chile peppers and sauté until browned, then add taco seasoning and 1/2 cup tomato sauce. Let simmer on low for 3 minutes. Meanwhile, make the cheese mixture. In a medium bowl mix eggs with cottage cheese and season with salt and pepper; stir until well blended. Preheat oven to 350 degrees F. To assemble the casserole, layer the bottom of 9x13 inch baking dish with 1/2 the tomato sauce, top that with the meat mixture. Place a layer of "healthified" tortillas, then top that with 1/2 the cottage cheese mixture. Place a layer of Monterrey Jack cheese on top of the cottage cheese. Repeat the layering one more time. Top with tomato sauce and remaining shredded cheese. Bake at 350 degrees F for 30 minutes or until cheese is melted and bubbly.

Makes 6 servings. NUTRITIONAL COMPARISON (per serving)
Traditional Casserole = 548 calories, 31g fat, 33g protein, 34.4g carbs, 4g fiber (30.4g effective carbs)
"Healthified" Casserole = 417 calories, 30g fat, 38.7g protein, 6.9g carbs, 3.5g fiber (3.4g effective carbs)

Enchiladas

Ingredients:

4 large cabbage leaves
16 oz. raw chicken breast
1/2 c. chopped onion
1 c. freshly shredded cheddar cheese, divided
1 c. plus 4 TBS enchilada sauce, divided
OPTIONAL TOPPINGS: sour cream, chopped scallions

Directions...
Preheat oven to 400 degrees F. In a pot, boil water and place large leaves of cabbage in the water. Boil for 5-7 minutes or until tender. Bring a skillet (with a little coconut oil) to medium-high heat. Add onions and chicken and cook for 4 minutes per side. Cook until chicken is cooked through and onion begins to brown, about 2 more minutes. Set aside. (OPTION: place frozen chicken breasts and onions in a crock pot before you leave work...they will be tender and cooked when you get home). Once chicken is cool enough to handle, place in a bowl and shred using two forks; one to hold the chicken in place and the other to scrape across the meat. Add 1/2 cup cheese, and 4 TBS enchilada sauce to the bowl with the chicken. Mix well and set aside. Lay cabbage tortillas out flat, and evenly distribute chicken mixture between the centers. Wrap the cabbage tortillas up tightly, and place them in the baking pan with the seam sides down. Pour remaining enchilada sauce over the enchiladas. Bake in the oven until hot, about 10 minutes. Evenly sprinkle remaining cheese over the enchiladas. Bake in the oven until cheese has melted, about 2 more minutes. Place on a plate and top with sour cream and scallions.

Serves 4. NUTRITIONAL COMPARISON (per serving):
Using Corn Tortilla = 430 calories, 17g fat, 40g protein, 22g carbs, 2.2g fiber (19.8g effective carbs)
Using cabbage tortilla = 350 calories, 17g fat, 40g protein, 5.7g carbs, 2g fiber (3.7g effective carbs)

Jicama Tacos

Ingredients:

6 Thin slices of jicama
6 oz. grass fed ground beef
2 c. organic leaf lettuce

Salsa
Sour Cream
1 Lime, cut into wedges

Directions... Slice jicama into very thin slices, using an electric slicer or mandolin slicer. Cook the beef in the Taco Seasoning Mix (see below). Fold the jicama slices into taco shells; fill with lettuce, meat, sour cream and salsa. Squirt the lime juice into each jicama shell and enjoy!

NUTRITIONAL COMPARISON (per 2 taco shells)
Traditional Taco Shell = 120 calories, 6g fat, 2g protein, 16g carbs, 2g fiber (14g effective carbs)
Jicama Taco Shell = 12 calories, 0g fat, trace protein, 2.6g carb, 1.5g fiber (1.1g effective carbs)

Taco Seasoning Ingredients:

2 TBS Chili Powder	1/2 tsp crushed Red Pepper Flakes	3 tsp ground Cumin
1/2 tsp Garlic Powder	1/2 tsp dried Oregano	2 tsp Celtic Sea Salt
1/2 tsp Onion Powder	1 tsp Paprika	2 tsp fresh ground black Pepper

Directions... In a bowl, mix together chili powder, garlic powder, onion powder, red pepper flakes, oregano, paprika, cumin, salt and pepper. Store in an airtight container.

Makes 20 servings. NUTRITIONAL COMPARISON (per serving)
Store Bought Taco Seasoning = 20 calories, 4 carbs, 0 fiber   "Healthified" Taco Seasoning = 5 calories, 0.9 carbs, 0.4g fiber

Fish Tacos

Ingredients:

FISH:
1 TBS coconut oil
Celtic sea salt and pepper to taste
6 (3 oz.) fillets mahi mahi fillets

SAUCE:
1/3 c. sour cream
1 TBS lime juice
1 tsp minced fresh ginger root
1/4 tsp ground cumin
1 dash cayenne pepper

ADDITIONS:
1 avocado - peeled, pitted and diced
1 c. salsa
6 (6 inch) "healthified" tortillas, warmed (see page 20)
1 c. chopped fresh cilantro

Directions... Heat the oil in a large skillet over medium-high heat. Season the mahi-mahi with salt and pepper. Cook the fillets in the hot oil until the fish is golden brown on each side, and no longer translucent in the center, about 3 minutes per side. Meanwhile, whisk together the sour cream, lime juice, ginger, cumin, cayenne pepper, salt and pepper to taste; set aside. To assemble, place a cooked mahi-mahi fillet into the center of a warmed "healthified" tortilla. Place a scoop of the avocado and salsa onto the fish, then drizzle with the sour cream sauce, and finish with a generous pinch of chopped cilantro.

NUTRITIONAL COMPARISON (per tortilla)
Traditional Tortilla = 140 calories, 3g fat, 4g protein, 25g carbs, trace fiber (25g effective carbs)
Almond Flour Tortilla = 105 calories, 7.5g fat, 4.1g protein, 5.6g carb, 3.8g fiber (1.8g effective carbs)
Coconut Flour Tortilla = 71 calories, 2.6g fat, 3.4g protein, 7.4g carbs, 5.2g fiber (2.2g effective carbs)

Ingredients:

"TORTILLA":
Coconut oil/butter/peanut oil
    for frying
3 eggs, separated
1/4 c. Jay Robb unflavored
    egg white or whey protein
2 oz. cream cheese, softened

FILLING:
2 c. Cauliflower "Rice"
2 c. Organic Lettuce
1 lb Organic Chicken/Beef/Pork Loin
1 jar Marinated Peppers
1 c. Salsa
1 avocado

Directions..."TORTILLA":

Separate the eggs (save the yolks for a different recipe), and whip the whites in a clean, dry, cool bowl for a few minutes until VERY stiff). Blend in the whey protein. Slowly stir in the cream cheese (without breaking down the whites). Heat the oil in a fry pan on medium high until a drop of water will sizzle. Once it is hot, place a circle of dough on the pan. Fry until golden brown on both sides. Remove from heat and place on a plate. Fill with your desired burrito filling and enjoy! Makes 4 servings.

CAULIFLOWER RICE: Cut the cauliflower into pieces and pulse in a food processor until small pieces of "rice." TIP: You can also use the heart of the cauliflower for rice, or use for making "French Fries." Set aside "rice." (TIP: can do this up to 2 days ahead of time and store in fridge for easy lunch/dinner options).

CHICKEN OR BEEF FILLING: Place chicken breasts, beef roast, or pork tenderloin in a crock pot on low (I also dumped a jar of organic salsa in the crock pot). Cook on low for 6-8 hours or until you can pull the meat apart with a fork. When you get home you have awesome shredded meat to fill the tortillas with.

Makes 4 servings. NUTRITIONAL COMPARISON (per tortilla)

Chipotle Tortilla =
290 calories, 9g fat, 7g protein, 44g carbs, 2g fiber (42g effective carbs)

"Healthified" Tortilla =
126 calories, 8g fat, 11g protein, 1g carb, trace fiber (1g effective carbs)

NUTRITIONAL COMPARISON (per burrito)

Chipotle Burrito (with rice, chicken, corn salsa, cheese, sour cream and guac) =
1975 calories, 104g fat, 56g protein, 179g carbs, 20g fiber (159g effective carbs)

"Healthified" Burrito =
310 calories, 18g fat, 15g protein, 8g carbs, 3g fiber (5g effective carbs)

Focaccia

Ingredients:

1 1/4 c. blanched almond flour
    (or 1/2 c. coconut flour)
5 TBS psyllium husk powder
    (no substitutes)
2 tsp baking powder
1 tsp Celtic sea salt
1 tsp garlic powder
1 tsp dried oregano
1 tsp dried thyme
1/2 tsp basil leaves
2 egg whites (8 egg whites if
    using coconut flour)
1 c. boiling marinara sauce
3-4 thinly slices of tomato
1 tsp rosemary

OPTIONAL TOPPINGS:
onion
grated Parmesan
olives
artichokes

Directions...
Preheat the oven to 350 degrees F. In a medium sized bowl, combine the almond/coconut flour, psyllium powder (no substitutes: flaxseed meal won't work), baking powder, salt, garlic, oregano, thyme, basil. Add in the eggs and combine until a thick dough. Boil the marinara and add into the bowl. Mix until well combined. Let sit for a minute or two until the dough gels up. Form the dough into a round "focaccia bread" shape (the dough will rise and spread a little) and place onto a greased piece of parchment paper and place on a baking sheet. Top with thinly sliced tomatoes and sprinkle with rosemary (and additional desired toppings). Bake for 65 minutes or until done all the way through. Remove from the oven and allow the bread cool. Serve with quality olive oil and balsamic vinegar.

Makes 5 servings.
NUTRITIONAL COMPARISON (per tortilla)

Traditional Bread =
180 calories, 6g fat, 4g protein, 41 carbs, trace fiber (41g effective carbs)
Almond Flour Sub =
180 calories, 12g fat, 7.3g protein, 10.8g carb, 7.6g fiber (3.2g effective carbs)
Coconut Flour Bread =
137 calories, 1.3g fat, 14.6g protein, 15g carbs, 10.4g fiber (4.6g effective carbs)

Mint

FUN HERB FACT

Mint counteracts nausea and vomiting, promote digestion, calm stomach muscle spasms, relieve flatulence, and ease hiccups. Menthol, the aromatic oil in peppermint, also relaxes the airways and fights bacteria and viruses. Menthol interferes with the sensation from pain receptors, thus it may be useful in reducing headache pain.

Gyros

Ingredients:

"HEALTHIFIED" PITA BREAD
1 1/4 c. blanched almond flour
    (or 1/2 c. coconut flour)
5 TBS psyllium husk powder
    (no substitutes)
2 tsp baking powder
1 tsp Celtic sea salt
2 egg whites (8 egg whites if
    using coconut flour)
1 c. boiling veggie broth OR water
    (broth adds flavor)
OPTIONAL: 1 tsp garlic powder

GYRO MEAT:
1/4 c. macadamia nut or olive oil
2 TBS lemon juice
1 clove garlic, crushed
1 tsp Celtic sea salt and pepper
1/2 tsp dried marjoram
1/8 tsp ground dried thyme
1/8 tsp ground dried rosemary
1/8 tsp dried oregano
1 lb boneless lamb (or beef)
    shoulder, cut into 1-inch cubes

SAUCE:
1 c. plain yogurt or coconut kefir
1/2 cucumber, shredded
1 clove garlic, minced
1 TBS lemon juice
1 tsp Celtic sea salt
4 (10 inch) bamboo skewers,
    soaked in water for 20 minutes

TOPPINGS:
1 tomato, sliced
1/4 red onion, thinly sliced
1 c. organic lettuce

Directions...

Preheat the oven to 350 degrees F. In a medium sized bowl, stir together the almond or coconut flour, psyllium husks, salt, baking powder and spices. Add the eggs. Stir continuously as you add the hot broth or water. Combine until very smooth. Separate into 4 even balls of dough. Flatten the dough into 'pita' shapes. Place the pita dough onto a greased cookie sheet. Bake at 350 degrees F for 65 minutes or until done throughout (this will depend on how thick the pitas are). Let cool, then cut each pita in 1/2. Use for gyros! Yum!

Makes 6 servings. NUTRITIONAL COMPARISON (per pita)
Traditional Pita Bread =
170 calories, 3g fat, 2g protein, 35 carbs, 3g fiber (32g effective carbs)
"Healthified" Almond Flour Pita =
139 calories, 129.4g fat, 5.6g protein, 8.8g carbs, 6g fiber (2.8g effective carbs)
"Healthified" Coconut Flour Pita =
121 calories, 0.7g fat, 21.3g protein, 10.7g carbs, 7g fiber (3.7g effective carbs)

Whisk together the oil, 2 TBS lemon juice, crushed garlic, 1 tsp salt and pepper, marjoram, thyme, rosemary, and oregano in a bowl, and pour into a resealable plastic bag. Add the cubed lamb, coat with the marinade, squeeze out excess air, and seal the bag. Marinate in the refrigerator 12 to 24 hours. Once the meat has finished marinating, remove from the refrigerator, and allow to stand at room temperature for 1 hour. Meanwhile, prepare the tzatziki sauce by whisking together the yogurt (if you use Coconut Kefir, which I recommend, add 1/8 tsp guar gum/ xanthan gum to thicken) and cucumber in a mixing bowl along with 1 clove of minced garlic, 1 TBS lemon juice, and 1 tsp salt. Cover the sauce and refrigerate until ready to use.

Preheat the oven's broiler and set the oven rack about 4 inches from the heat source. Remove the lamb cubes from the marinade. Discard the remaining marinade. Spray a broiling pan with cooking spray, thread the meat onto the skewers, and place the skewers onto the prepared pan. Broil under the preheated broiler to your desired degree of doneness, turning every few minutes so the meat cooks evenly. It should take about 10 minutes to cook the meat to medium-well.

To assemble the sandwiches, split each piece in half, and open up the pockets. Divide the tomato and onion slices among the pocket bread halves. Stuff with lettuce, then fill with the broiled lamb. Sprinkle with crumbled feta cheese, and top with the tzatziki sauce to serve.

Makes 4 sandwiches. NUTRITIONAL COMPARISON (per gyro)
Traditional Gyro =
497 calories, 24g fat, 40.6g protein, 43g carbs, 4g fiber (39g effective carbs)
"Healthified" Gyro using yogurt sauce =
440 calories, 26g fat, 40.6g protein, 14g carbs, 8g fiber (6g effective carbs)
"Healthified" Gyro using kefir sauce =
399 calories, 21g fat, 38g protein, 12.5g carbs, 8g fiber (4.5g effective carbs)

Leptin

Did you ever wonder why it is easier to gain weight than keep it off? The key is in the fat cells where a powerful hormone is produced called leptin. Leptin signals the brain to regulate the metabolism in order to store or to burn fat. 85% of people who lose weight, end up regaining weight because the "metabolic thermostat" of the body, leptin, is automatically reset upward. When people lose weight, leptin production decreases, which causes people to regain lost weight. This protein hormone is derived from fat cells so when you lose fat, leptin levels drop. When you gain fat, leptin levels rise. Once leptin is secreted by your fat cells, it travels to the hypothalamus; which controls eating behavior. Once it's there, leptin activates anorectic nerve cells, which decreases your appetite. At the same time, leptin stops cells from stimulating your appetite. To put it simply, when leptin levels drop, you get hungry. When they go up, you feel full. Leptin communicates directly with your brain, telling the brain how much fat is in storage. It controls appetite, energy, and metabolic rate. Leptin problems are the primary reason for food cravings, overeating, slow metabolism, food obsession and heart disease.

You'd think that having extra fat stores creates more leptin, but mysteriously, that is not the case. 98% of those who are significantly overweight are leptin-resistant. Most defects in leptin-signaling may lead to obesity, overeating and less energy expenditure. Leptin-resistance is similar to insulin-resistance in that it occurs after being overexposed to high levels of the hormone. At this point, the body no longer responds to the hormone. Much like high blood sugar levels result in surges in insulin, sugar metabolized in fat cells causes the fat to release surges in leptin. Over time, leptin-resistance may develop. The best way to reduce your chances of diabetes is to avoid surges in leptin; which is the leading cause of leptin-resistance. Eating the typical American diet, full of refined sugars and other processed foods, is a guaranteed way to cause undesired surges. Maintaining a diet including simple, unprocessed real foods is the best way to prevent leptin-resistance.

The main macro-nutrient that helps with leptin is protein. Aim to increase your protein to at least 30 grams for breakfast and at least another 60 throughout the day. Protein improves leptin sensitivity, which lowers calorie intake by helping you feel full faster. Choose quality proteins like salmon, grass fed meat, free-range eggs, and a quality whey protein, which all of my recipes are filled with! Happy Eating!

Calzone made with Toasted Sub Bread recipe. See page 22.

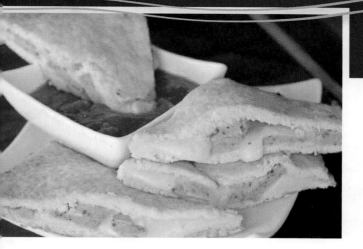

Ingredients:

1 1/2 c. zucchini/cauliflower or eggplant
1 egg
1 c. freshly shredded Parmesan or mozzarella (not that junk in a can!)
1/2 c. No sugar marinara (Mario Batali brand)
FAVORITE TOPPINGS:
(Bolinski's chicken sausage cut into slices, olives, mushrooms)
1 c. freshly shredded cheese

Directions... If using eggplant: Peel the outside off and cut up eggplant into long lasagna noodle-shaped strips. Place on a sprayed cookie sheet, sprinkle with salt and bake for 15 minutes (to get some moisture out). Preheat oven to 450 degrees F. In a food processor, blend eggplant/zucchini/cauliflower, egg and cheese. Grease a cookie sheet and form a large circle with the dough, making sure to make the thickness even (don't forget to grease the cookie sheet!). Bake for 10 minutes, or until the edges are brown. Flip the crust. Turn oven temperature to 375 degrees F. On one half of the circle, top with toppings, careful to stay at least an inch from the edges. Around the edge of the crust, sprinkle a small amount of mozzarella cheese. Fold crust over and press edges together firmly with your fingers by pressing down on the pan (the cheese will melt and hold crust together). Bake for another 20 minutes, or until top is sufficiently golden-brown. Serve with no sugar marinara for dipping.

Makes 2 servings. NUTRITIONAL COMPARISON (per serving)
Traditional Calzone = 770 calories, 28g fat, 39g protein, 87g carbs, 3g fiber (85g effective)
"Healthified" Eggplant Calzone = 369 calories, 26g fat, 29.7g protein, 11g carbs, 4.1g fiber (6.9g effective)
"Healthified" Zucchini Calzone = 394 calories, 26g fat, 30g protein, 10.4g carbs, 2.9g fiber (7.1g effective)
"Healthified" Cauliflower Calzone = 400 calories, 26g fat, 30g protein, 11.5g carbs, 3.9g fiber (7.6g effective)

Ingredients:

1 eggplant
2 eggs beaten
1/2 c. almond flour
1/2 c. Parmesan cheese, grated
2 TBS oregano
2 TBS garlic powder
1 TBS onion powder
MARINARA SAUCE
(Mario Batali brand no soybean oil and no sugar added)

When choosing a marinara sauce, check the ingredients for sugar. Quality tomatoes don't need extra sugar for sweetness. This also increases unneeded carbohydrates. My rule when choosing a marinara is to stay under 5 carbs per 1/2 cup and it should use olive oil ... never soybean oil.

Directions... Peel eggplant and cut into "breadstick" shapes. In a bowl, whisk eggs. Set aside. In another bowl mix almond flour, cheese and spices. Place eggplant sticks into egg mix, then roll in almond flour mixture.

OPTION 1: Preheat oven to 400 degrees F. Bake on a greased cookie sheet for 15-20 minutes or until golden brown.
OPTION 2: Fry in a pan with coconut oil until golden brown. Serve with marinara sauce.

Makes 12 servings. NUTRITIONAL COMPARISON (per "breadstick"):
Traditional Breadstick = 150 calories, 6g fat, 4g protein, 20g carbs, 0g fiber (20g effective carbs)
"Healthified" Breadstick = 66 calories, 4.2g fat, 4g protein, 3.4g carbs, 1.8g fiber (1.6g effective carbs)

Did you know that a 200 calorie bagel with fat free cream cheese for a total of 250 calories for breakfast can cause weight gain? I love this fact from the book "Wheat Belly": "Did you know that eating two slices of WHOLE WHEAT bread can increase blood sugar more than 2 tablespoons of pure sugar can?" Workout warriors and chronic dieters cut out fat and consume the so called healthy "whole grains" yet the scale doesn't budge. Calories in and calories out is one big fat lie!

1. INSULIN: High carbohydrate, fat-free foods, such as wheat, rice, brown rice, oatmeal, corn, potatoes, bananas increase blood sugar and therefore insulin. These foods are very high on the glycemic index. When we eat foods high on the glycemic index, this will cause insulin to rise. This abuse of high insulin levels, increases our risk of insulin resistance. Insulin resistance causes fat cells to grow, mainly in abdomen as well as the snowball effect of health conditions like pre-diabetes. The more visceral fat you accumulate, the worse insulin resistance becomes; thus the vicious cycle ensues.

2. LEPTIN: Did you ever wonder why it is easier to gain weight as compared to keeping it off? The key to this is in the fat cells where a powerful hormone is produced called leptin. Leptin signals the brain to regulate the metabolism in order to store or to burn fat. Once leptin is secreted by your fat cells, it travels to the hypothalamus; which controls eating behavior. Once it's there, leptin activates anorectic nerve cells, which decreases your appetite. At the same time, leptin stops cells from stimulating your appetite. To put it simply, when leptin levels drop, you get hungry. When they go up, you feel full. The lectin in wheat has the potential to block the leptin receptor. Leptin resistance is increasingly looking like a fundamental reason why people struggle to lose weight. . Leptin-resistance is similar to insulin-resistance in that it occurs after being overexposed to high levels of the hormone. At this point, the body no longer responds to the hormone. Much like high blood sugar levels result in surges in insulin, sugar metabolized in fat cells causes the fat to release surges in leptin. Over time, leptin-resistance may develop. The best way to reduce your chances of diabetes is to avoid surges in leptin; which is the leading cause of leptin-resistance. Eating the typical American diet, full of refined sugars and other processed foods, is a guaranteed way to cause undesired surges. Focusing your diet on simple, unprocessed real foods like vegetables is currently the best way to prevent leptin-resistance.

3. HUNGER: When blood sugar goes up, it also must come down. This is why people who eat a high carb breakfast have a hard time making it to lunch; they become irritable and they have a foggy brain about 2 hours after the bagel with fat-free cream cheese. This undesired feeling is cured with a dose of carbs; creating a vicious cycle. Not only that, it stimulates unruly cravings for sugar.

4. ADDICTION: The protein found in wheat is an altered amino acid and looks totally different than it's non-genetically modified ancestor. They basically act as appetite stimulants. The gliadins that are in today's wheat are morphine-like polypeptides that enter the brain called exorphins. A VERY interesting fact is that these exorphins can be blocked by opiate-blocking drugs. A drug company has filed an application with the FDA for a weight loss indication for an opiate-based drug because clinical studies found volunteers lost 22 pounds after 6 months. Volunteers taking the opiate blocker reduced calorie intake by 400 calories per day. This is so fascinating because there is only one food that has opiate-like compounds in the body...yep, it is wheat.

5. DEPRESSION: After the digestive tract, the most commonly affected system to be affected by gluten is the nervous system. It is thought that depression can be caused by gluten in one of two ways. The first area addresses the inflammatory changes gluten can cause. A gluten-sensitive individual's immune system responds to the protein gliadin. Unfortunately, that protein is similar in structure to other proteins present in the body, including those of the brain and nerve cells. A cross reactivity can occur whereby the immune system "confuses" proteins in the body for the protein gliadin. This is called cellular mimicry and the result is the body attacking its own tissues with inflammation resulting. When inflammation happens in the brain and nervous system, a variety of symptoms can occur, including depression. Research shows us that patients with symptoms involving the nervous system suffer from digestive problems only 13% of the time. This is significant because mainstream medicine equates gluten sensitivity almost exclusively with digestive complaints. Gluten interferes with protein absorption. Specifically the amino acid tryptophan can be deficient. Tryptophan is a protein in the brain responsible for a feeling of well-being and relaxation. A deficiency causes depression and anxiety. 90% of serotonin production occurs in the digestive tract. So it makes sense that food might have an effect, either positive or negative, on serotonin production.

Thin Crust Pizza

Ingredients:

1/3 c. almond flour
1/3 c. unflavored whey/egg white protein
1/3 c. Parmesan cheese, shredded
1 tsp Celtic sea salt
Water (just enough to hold dough together)

OPTIONAL:
Italian spices
Pizza Toppings of your choice

Directions...

Preheat oven to 375 degrees F. In a large bowl, mix all the dry ingredients together. Slowly add in water, 1 TBS at a time until dough can hold a ball shape. Grease a pie pan. With wet fingers, spread the dough being sure to cover the pie pan. Bake for 15 minutes or until golden brown. Remove from oven. Top with no sugar marinara sauce, your favorite pizza toppings and mozzarella. Place back in oven for 5 minutes or until cheese is melted.

Makes 2 servings.
NUTRITIONAL COMPARISON (per serving)

Traditional Frozen Pizza =
350 calories, 16g fat, 10g protein, 54g carbs, 5g fiber (49g effective carbs)

"Healthified" Pizza CRUST Only =
220 calories, 14g fat, 22g protein, 5g carbs, 2g fiber (3g effective carbs)

FUN FACT

For every molecule of sugar we ingest, our bodies uses 54 molecules of magnesium to process it!

No matter where the carbohydrates come from; 4 grams of carbohydrates equal one teaspoon of sugar in our body. Let me say that again…4 grams of carbohydrates equal 1 teaspoon of sugar in our body. So with that thought, a small Blizzard has 530 calories and 83 grams of carbohydrates; which equals 21 teaspoons of sugar. A nine ounce bag of potato chips equals 32 teaspoons of sugar…add a soda, that's another 16 teaspoons of sugar.

Are your kids having a hard time falling asleep? Most people are deficient in magnesium, including children. A magnesium deficiency can have serious consequences, including low serotonin. Magnesium and serotonin don't just help to regulate your mood, they also can affect your physiology in many ways. Serotonin is a neurotransmitter that sends signals of satiety, satisfaction and relaxation. It also regulates our appetite and influences sleep cycles; if serotonin is low, melatonin will be low. So low magnesium can lead to over-eating, depression, insomnia and other serious issues including migraine headaches. Almonds are high in magnesium, so

Serve with Twisted
Breadsticks made
with the Toasted
Sub Bread recipe.
See page 22.

(Take two pieces of dough and twist
them around each other....then bake)

White Crab Lasagna

Ingredients:

3/4 c. minced shallots
8 TBS butter
1/2 tsp grated nutmeg
6 TBS cream cheese
3/4 c. chicken stock
2 large eggs, lightly beaten
1/2 tsp Celtic sea salt and pepper
1/4 pound grated Parmigiano-Reggiano (1 c.), divided
1 pound deli shaved chicken breast or ham
6 c. freshly shredded mozzarella cheese

OPTIONAL:
artichokes
capers
mushrooms
peppers
or my favorite addition CRAB! LOTS of crab!

Directions...
Preheat oven to 350 degrees F with rack in middle. Cook shallots in butter in a heavy medium saucepan over medium heat, stirring occasionally, until tender, about 4 minutes. Add nutmeg, then slowly whisk in cream cheese and stock. Bring to a boil, whisking, then simmer, stirring occasionally, just until sauce lightly coats back of spoon, about 1 minute. Remove from heat and cool to warm, stirring occasionally. Stir in eggs, sea salt, 1/2 teaspoon pepper, and 1/2 cup Parmigiano-Reggiano cheese. Spread about 1 1/4 cups sauce over bottom of an 11- by 8-inch baking dish. Cover with a layer of shaved chicken (for the "noodles"), then additional fillings such as artichokes, mushrooms, capers and crab if desired. Top with 2 cups shredded mozzarella. Repeat layering 3 more times, then top with remaining sauce and remaining 1/2 cup Parmigiano-Reggiano cheese. Bake, uncovered, until browned, 45 to 55 minutes.

Makes 12 servings.
NUTRITIONAL COMPARISON (per cup):
White Flour Noodles = 246 calories, 43g carbs, 5g fiber (38g effective carbs)
"Healthified" Noodles = 84 calories, 2g carb, 0g fiber (2g effective carbs)

NUTRITIONAL COMPARISON (per serving)

Traditional White Lasagna =
439 calories, 26g fat, 22g protein, 31g carbs, 0.9g fiber (30.1g effective carbs)

"Healthified" White Lasagna =
376 calories, 28g fat, 25g protein, 5.5g carbs, 0.5g fiber (5g effective carbs)

"Healthified" Lasagna with artichokes, capers and crab =
394 calories, 28g fat, 29g protein, 7.4g carbs, 1.4g fiber (6g effective carbs)

Five Cheese "Ziti"

Ingredients:

SAUCE:
4 c. tomato sauce
2 c. Alfredo sauce
1/2 c. ricotta cheese
1/4 c. mozzarella cheese, shredded
3 TBS Fontina cheese, shredded
1 clove garlic, minced

TOPPING :
3 c. mozzarella cheese, shredded
1/2 c. blanched almond flour
3 TBS Romano cheese, grated
3 TBS Parmesan cheese, grated
1 TBS fresh garlic, chopped
3 TBS melted butter or macadamia nut oil
3 TBS fresh flat-leaf Italian parsley, chopped

REMAINING INGREDIENTS:
6 packages Fettuccine Miracle Noodles, or
    2 large zucchini/daikon made into "noodles"
1 c. mozzarella cheese, shredded

Directions...
To prepare the "ziti" sauce, combine all ingredients for the Ziti Sauce in a large bowl; cover and refrigerate until ready to use. Next, prepare the topping. In a medium-size bowl, whisk together the first four ingredients for the Ziti Topping. Add the garlic, oil, and parsley and mix until thoroughly blended. Cover and refrigerate until ready to use.

When you are ready to eat, preheat oven to 375 degrees F. Rinse and drain the Miracle Noodles (or make your veggie into "pasta"). Pour 1/2 cup of prepared ziti sauce into a very large dish, and spread it evenly over the bottom using a spoon. Drain the pasta well and put on top of the sauce in the dish, then top with remaining sauce. Mix thoroughly. Spread 1 cup of shredded mozzarella over the pasta and sauce mixture. Top the mozzarella with the prepared Ziti Topping, spreading evenly. Place pan on center oven rack and bake until top is golden brown and cheese is bubbling, about 30 to 40 minutes. Remove and serve immediately.

Makes 8 servings.
NUTRITIONAL COMPARISON (per serving)
Traditional Ziti using White Noodles =
624 calories, 27g fat, 30g protein, 54g carbs, 3g fiber (51g effective carbs)
"Healthified" Ziti =
425 calories, 27g fat, 23.5g protein, 8g carbs, 2g fiber (6g effective carbs)

Gout, or elevated levels of uric acid, is one of the most misunderstood problem that the medical field is trying to fix with a diet that is low in protein and high in fructose. The prevalence of gout seems to have doubled over the last 25 years. Uric acid accumulates and crystallizes into needle-sharp urate crystals. These crystals then lodge in the soft tissues and in the joints of the extremities, most commonly the big toe. This causes inflammation, swelling and terrible pain. Uric acid is a breakdown of protein compounds known as purines, which are the building blocks of amino acids. High concentrations of purines are found in meat, SO we assumed that the primary cause of elevated uric acid levels in the blood is caused by an excess of meat consumption. The actual cause has been quite shocking! Just as low sodium diet has been proven to NOT to help with lowering blood pressure; and a cholesterol-free diet doesn't help with decreasing heart disease, a low-purine diet has no effect on uric acid levels! A vegetarian diet will drop serum uric acid levels by only about 10% compared to a typical American diet, but that isn't going to do much to decrease the gout and the pain that is being experienced. Another shocking piece of evidence is that eating additional protein increases the excretion of uric acid from the kidney! This decreases the level of uric acid in the blood; therefore the high protein diets are helpful, even if the purines aren't.

Now let's look at the true culprit: insulin resistance DOES raise uric acid levels. This happens because it decreases uric acid elimination by the kidney; the same way it raises blood pressure by decreasing sodium excretion. So raised insulin levels will raise uric acid levels and can cause gout. Therefore a high carbohydrate diet is one large problem with gout. BUT there is one specific carbohydrate source to REALLY steer clear from! Fructose causes many problems, but we are now understanding that it also is a main contributor to gout. Fructose increases serum levels of uric acid. The increase in uric acid levels with an infusion of fructose was first written about in the Lancet in the late 1960s. Fructose was proven to accelerate the breakdown ATP (the primary source of energy); which is loaded with purines. ATP stands for adenosine triphosphate; adenosine is a form of adenine, and adenine is a purine; this increases production of uric acid. Alcohol also raises uric acid levels through the same reaction. Fructose also stimulates the production of purines. The metabolism of fructose leads to the production of lactic acid, which inhibits the excretion of uric acid by the kidney, which raises uric acid by that mechanism.

Gout can run in families. In 1990, Edwin Seegmiller and the British geneticist George Radda, discovered that the familial association was a very specific gene defect that regulated fructose metabolism. This gene defect made it difficult to metabolize fructose and cause a predisposition to having gout if the diet had excess fructose. So where do we get this excess fructose? Sugar is about 50% fructose, honey is about 55% fructose, high fructose corn syrup can range up to 65% fructose, and AGAVE is about 90% fructose! Keep in mind that natural foods, even fruit, has fructose and in extreme health conditions, they should be avoided.

Garlic Bread

Ingredients:

6 egg whites
1 tsp cream of tartar
1/2 c. unflavored egg white or
    whey protein
1/4 c. cream cheese, softened
Cloves of garlic (or garlic powder)
Butter or macadamia nut oil

OPTIONAL: Mozzarella cheese

NOTE: Whipping the whites properly is tricky, do not under-whip or this won't turn out. "If you need a little help keeping the egg white from falling, try adding xanthan gum to the whites. It acts as a stabilizer."

Directions...
Whip the whites with the cream of tartar for a few minutes until VERY stiff. Very slowly add in whey protein. Fold the cream cheese and seasonings to the whipped whites. Grease a bread pan very well. Spoon the mixture into the pan and smooth the top with a spatula. Bake at 375 degrees F for 45 minutes until lightly browned. Cool before cutting, then cut into 12 pieces. I also spread a little butter on each piece, rubbed with garlic cloves and sprinkled with cheese. I tossed it back into the oven on a broil for 3 minutes until butter was bubbly and lightly browned.

Serves 12. NUTRITIONAL COMPARISON:

Pepperidge Farm Garlic Bread =
170 Calories, 7g fat, 4g protein, 24g carbs, 2g fiber (22g effective carbs)

"Healthified" Garlic Bread =
43 calories, 2g fat, 5.6g protein, 1g carb, 0g fiber (1g effective carbs)

Mousakka

Makes 8 servings.
NUTRITIONAL COMPARISON (per serving) =
Traditional Moussaka = 416 calories, 24g fat,
13g protein, 37g carbs, 9g fiber (28g effective carbs)
"Healthified" Moussaka = 421 calories, 23.3g fat,
37.6g protein, 16.9g carbs, 7.5g fiber (9.4g effective carbs)

Ingredients:

EGGPLANT LAYER:
3 large eggplants
Pinch of Celtic sea salt and
    freshly ground black pepper
Coconut oil or butter

CHEESE SAUCE:
4 TBS Butter
1/2 c. beef broth
2 eggs, separated
8 oz. feta cheese, crumbled
1 to 2 c. freshly grated Parmesan
Pinch of nutmeg

MEAT LAYER:
1/2 medium onion, chopped
2 garlic cloves, minced
1/2 lemon, sliced in thin circles
1 handful fresh oregano leaves, chopped
2 handfuls fresh flat-leaf parsley, chopped
1 1/2 pounds ground lamb or grass fed beef
2 c. finely chopped mushrooms
1 cinnamon stick
1/4 tsp nutmeg
1 (16 oz.) can Contadina Thick and
    Zesty Tomato Sauce

Directions... To prepare the eggplants: Cut off the stems, remove the skin with a vegetable peeler, and cut lengthwise into 1/2-inch thick slices. Season all the pieces of eggplant with salt and pepper on both sides. Coat a large skillet with oil and heat over medium flame. Fry the eggplant in a single layer, turning once, until brown on both sides. Drain the eggplant on a paper towel-lined platter. OR Preheat oven to 350 degrees F. Prepare eggplant into 1/2 inch thick slices, lay on greased cookie sheet, sprinkle with salt and pepper and bake in oven for 15 minutes or until soft.

MEAT LAYER: Add a little more oil to the pan and toss in the onion, garlic, lemon slices, oregano, and parsley. Cook and stir until soft and fragrant, about 3 minutes. Add the ground lamb and mushrooms (this will "lighten" the dish) stirring to break up the meat; season with salt and pepper, and toss in the cinnamon stick. Stir in the tomato sauce. Simmer until the liquid has evaporated, stirring occasionally. Remove from the heat.

CHEESE SAUCE: In a saucepan, combine 4 TBS butter and broth; cook over low heat. Beat egg yolks, and combine with cheese and nutmeg; add to saucepan. Beat egg whites until stiff and fold into sauce. Preheat the oven to 350 degrees F. Line the bottom of a 9 by 13-inch glass or ceramic baking dish with 1/3 of the eggplant slices; they should completely cover the bottom. Spread 1/2 of the meat sauce over the eggplant, evening it out with a spatula. Sprinkle with 1/2 of the cheese sauce. Repeat the layers again, ending with a final layer of eggplant. Cover the top with a nice even layer of Parmesan cheese. Bake for 30 to 40 minutes or until the top is golden. Let cool 10 minutes before serving.

Protein Noodle Lasagna

Ingredients:

1 pound Italian sausage
¾ lb grass fed ground beef
1/2 small onion, chopped
2 cloves garlic, minced
1 jar no sugar marinara sauce

16 oz. ricotta cheese
1 egg
½ tsp Celtic sea salt
Thinly sliced nitrate free
    deli Chicken Breast
¾ lb mozzarella cheese, sliced
¾ c. Parmesan cheese

Directions... Preheat oven to 425 degrees. F In a Dutch oven, cook sausage, ground beef, onion, and garlic over medium heat until well browned. Stir in marinara sauce. In a mixing bowl, combine ricotta cheese with egg, and 1/2 tsp salt. To assemble, spread 1 1/2 cups of meat sauce in the bottom of a 9x13 inch baking dish. Arrange chicken breast slices over meat sauce. Spread with one half of the ricotta cheese mixture. Top with a third of mozzarella cheese slices. Spoon 1 1/2 cups meat sauce over mozzarella, and sprinkle with 1/4 cup Parmesan cheese. Repeat layers, and top with remaining mozzarella and Parmesan cheese. Cover with foil: to prevent sticking, either spray foil with cooking spray, or make sure the foil does not touch the cheese. Bake for 25 minutes. Remove foil, and bake an additional 25 minutes. Cool for 15 minutes before serving.

NUTRITIONAL COMPARISON (per cup):
Traditional Noodles = 246 calories, 0g fat, 1g protein, 43g carbs, 5g fiber (38g effective carbs)
"Healthified" Noodles = 84 calories, 1g fat, 20g protein, 2g carb, 0g fiber (2g effective carbs)

Zinc and Cravings

Are you suffering from intense cravings? It could be a zinc deficiency. Zinc is essential to blood sugar regulation by influencing carbohydrate metabolism, increasing insulin response, and improving glucose tolerance. Zinc influences basal metabolic rate, thyroid hormone activity, and improves taste sensitivity. The average American diet is already deficient in many minerals, but in someone who frequently diets...even more so! The best sources of zinc include oysters and red meat, neither of which is eaten frequently by many people. The average American consumes less than 10 mg of zinc per day, far less than what is required for normal sugar metabolism or the other functions of zinc in the body. Correcting a zinc deficiency (along with other minerals) can go a long way toward helping the frustrated dieter control impulses to eat something sweet, something fatty, or something devoid of nutrition in an attempt to satisfy an inner compulsion.

Zinc is also essential for keeping a healthy immune system, building proteins, triggering enzymes, and creating DNA. Zinc also helps the cells in your body communicate by functioning as a neurotransmitter. A deficiency in zinc can lead to stunted growth, diarrhea, impotence, hair loss, eye and skin lesions, impaired appetite, and depressed immunity.

Certain prescriptions, including birth control, deplete zinc in our body. A zinc deficiency could cause birth defects. So if you are planning on getting pregnant, a good rule of thumb is to discontinue birth control for 6 months before getting pregnant. Increasing your zinc through food is always the best choice, so we can maintain a proper copper-zinc balance. Grass-fed red meat and seafood are awesome sources.

Seafood Alfredo

Ingredients:

1 large zucchini (made into 6 c. of "pasta")
Shrimp, crab, scallops...whatever protein you enjoy
Fresh tomatoes, cut into slices

SAUCE:
1 stick butter
2 cloves garlic
4 TBS cream cheese
1/3 c. beef broth
1/2 c. Parmesan cheese

Directions...
SAUCE: Place butter in a sauce pan with garlic and cook until light golden brown, stir constantly, or the butter will burn. Turn to a low heat. Smash up garlic cloves in the butter. Stir in cream cheese, broth and Parmesan. Simmer for at least 15 minutes...the flavors open up if you simmer longer:) Serve over zucchini noodles and your choice of seafood.

Makes 4 servings. NUTRITIONAL COMPARISON (per serving)
Traditional Alfredo Pasta = 665 calories, 33g fat, 17g protein, 71g carbs, trace fiber (71g effective carbs)
"Healthified" Alfredo = 315 calories, 31g fat, 7.7g protein, 5.2g carbs, 1.3g fiber (3.9g effective carbs)

My suggestion is to only serve the sauce on the noodles you will eat that night. The leftover noodles and sauce get a little soggy, so reserve both separately. To find the awesome noodle maker: http://astore.amazon.com/marisnutran05-20/detail/B0000DDVYE

Lemon Cream "Pasta"

Ingredients:

2 TBS butter
3 large shallots, minced
1 1/4 c. organic beef broth
   (or veggie broth)
2 oz. cream cheese
2 tsp grated lemon peel
1/4 tsp cayenne pepper
2 TBS thinly sliced
   fresh mint leaves
1 TBS fresh lemon juice
Cherry tomatoes, cut thin
1 large zucchini
   (cut into noodle-like strips)
12 thin slices prosciutto
Freshly grated Parmesan cheese

Directions...

Melt butter in large nonstick skillet over medium heat. Add shallots and sauté until translucent, about 2 minutes. Add broth. Simmer over medium-high heat until mixture is reduced to 1/4 cup, about 2 minutes. Add cream cheese, lemon peel, cayenne and tomatoes (if using). Simmer until sauce thickens slightly, about 3 minutes. Stir in mint and lemon juice. Season sauce to taste with salt and pepper.

Meanwhile, cut the zucchini into "pasta." Toss pasta with sauce to coat. My suggestion is to only serve the sauce on the noodles you will eat that night. The leftover noodles and sauce get a little soggy, so reserve both separately. To find the awesome noodle maker: http://astore.amazon.com/marisnutran05-20/detail/B0000DDVYE

Divide "pasta" among plates or bowls. Drape prosciutto slices atop pasta and serve, adding Parmesan if desired.

Makes 2 LARGE servings!!!
NUTRITIONAL COMPARISON (per serving)
Traditional Pasta Dish (using white pasta and cream) =
859 calories, 28g fat, 12g protein, 142g carbs, 0.6g fiber (141g effective carbs)
"Healthified" Pasta =
257 calories, 22g fat, 7.5g protein, 8.4g carbs, 2.4g fiber (6g effective carbs)

White Pasta = 246 calories, 43g carbs, 0g fiber
Zucchini "noodles" = 20 calories, 4g carbs, 2g fiber

Quick Tip

Ease Anxiety

For 90% of dieters, a deficiency in one of four essential brain chemicals can cause weight gain, fatigue and stress. The solution to losing weight doesn't lie in deprivation diets; it lies in balancing our neurotransmitters. Specialized nutritionists, like myself, and advanced practitioners are focusing on how the brain affects our health.

1. Serotonin influences appetite.
2. GABA curbs emotional eating
3. Acetylcholine regulates fat storage
4. Dopamine controls metabolism

When these brain chemicals are balanced, our bodies are better able to lose those extra pounds. GABA is the primary neurotransmitter in the temporal lobe, the area of the brain that governs perception, attention, speech and motions. Low levels of this chemical have been linked to psychological symptoms such as insecurity, excessive worrying, fear of new experiences, poor concentration and lack of impulse control. But as GABA shortfalls are corrected, we can regain calmness, dependability and objectivity. GABA deficiency displays as anxiousness, nervousness, irritability, restlessness, allergies, blurred vision, clammy hands, butterflies in the stomach, dizziness, IBS, constipation, neuropathy, fibromyalgia, headache, insomnia, trembling or shaking, tinnitus, manic depression, and mood disorders. You don't need all of these issues to be deficient in GABA. To read more on how to increase GABA through foods and supplements, check out my book, "Secrets to Controlling Your Weight Cravings and Mood".

Eating foods high in fiber increases glutamic acid/glutamate which forms glutamine, an amino involved in the production of GABA. Cooking destroys amino acids so eat as many raw foods as possible, such as the zucchini in this recipe.

To find the Joyce Chen Spiral Slicer, go to:
http://astore.amazon.com/marisnutran05-20/detail/B0000DDVYE

"Pasta" Carbonara

Ingredients:

4 packages Miracle Noodles
   (or 2 medium zucchini)
8 slices bacon, chopped
1/2 c. onion, chopped
1 clove garlic, minced

1/4 c. fresh peas
   (optional...peas are a starch)
4 eggs
1/2 c. grated Parmesan cheese
1 pinch salt and black pepper to taste
2 TBS fresh parsley, chopped
2 TBS grated Parmesan cheese

Directions...
Open Miracle Noodles, rinse with water (a lot!) and drain. Pat dry and set aside. If you are using zucchini, cut the zucchini into "pasta." If you are using zucchini "pasta" my suggestion is to only serve the sauce on the noodles you will eat that night. The leftover noodles and sauce get a little soggy, so reserve both separately. To find the awesome noodle maker go here:
http://astore.amazon.com/marisnutran05-20/detail/B0000DDVYE
In a large skillet, cook chopped bacon until slightly crisp; remove and drain onto paper towels. Reserve 2 tablespoons of bacon fat and heat in reused large skillet. Add chopped onion, and cook over medium heat until onion is translucent. Add minced garlic and peas (if using), and cook for an additional 1 minute. Return cooked bacon to skillet; add cooked and drained spaghetti. Toss to coat and heat through. Add beaten eggs and cook, tossing constantly with tongs or large fork until eggs are barely set. Quickly add 1/2 cup Parmesan cheese, and toss again. Add salt and pepper to taste (remember that bacon and Parmesan are very salty). Serve immediately with chopped parsley sprinkled on top, and extra Parmesan cheese at table.

Makes 4 servings. NUTRITIONAL COMPARISON (per serving)
Traditional Carbonara = 523 calories, 15.5g fat, 28g protein, 66.2g carbs, 0.8g fiber (65.8g effective carbs)
"Healthified" Miracle Noodle Carbonara = 197 calories, 12.9g fat, 15.8g protein, 4g carbs, 0.8g fiber (3.2g effective carbs)
"Healthified" Zucchini Noodle Carbonara = 212 calories, 13g fat, 17g protein, 7.4g carbs, 1.9g fiber (5.5g effective carbs)

Pad Thai

Ingredients:

1 lb boneless, skinless chicken breast
    halves, cut into bite-size pieces
1/2 tsp Celtic sea salt and
    ground black pepper to taste
3/4 c. Swerve
1 tsp ground cayenne pepper
3 TBS white wine vinegar
6 TBSs fish sauce
1 TBS peanut butter or sunbutter
1 TBS coconut oil
5 cloves garlic, minced
4 large eggs, lightly beaten
1/2 c. fresh bean sprouts
2 packages Miracle Noodles
2 c. beef broth
1/2 c. chopped green onion

Directions...

Bring a large pot of water to a boil. Season chicken with salt and black pepper; set aside. Whisk natural sweetener, cayenne pepper, white wine vinegar, fish sauce, and sunbutter or peanut butter together in a bowl. Coat the inside of a large skillet or wok with olive oil and place over high heat. Cook and stir chicken in the hot oil just until the meat is white outside but still pink inside, about 3 minutes. Remove chicken and set aside in a bowl. Lower the heat under the skillet to medium-low. Cook and stir garlic in the skillet until it becomes translucent, 1 to 2 minutes. Cook and stir eggs into garlic until loosely cooked, 2 to 3 minutes. Pour peanut sauce into the garlic and eggs, and stir to combine. Bring sauce to a simmer. Return chicken to the skillet with eggs and sauce. Simmer until chicken is no longer pink in the center and the juices run clear, stirring frequently, 5 to 8 more minutes. Stir bean sprouts, Miracle noodles, and beef broth into the skillet. Bring to a simmer, and cook for about 10 minutes. Sprinkle with green onions to serve.

Makes 5 servings.
NUTRITIONAL COMPARISON (per serving)
Pad Thai with Rice Noodles and sugar =
601 calories, 20.2g fat, 42.6g protein, 59g carbs, 2.6g fiber (56.4 effective carbs)
"Healthified" Pad Thai =
311 calories, 15.8g fat, 36.3g protein, 4.8g carbs, 1g fiber (3.8 effective carbs)

Why Tamari Sauce

You may look at the ingredients and see "Tamari" sauce and say, "what?" So what is it? and why ORGANIC? Monsanto Co., the world's largest seed producer, has developed the first-generation Roundup Ready soybean (and corn) seeds...they are in discussion about putting Roundup INSIDE the seed so the weeds have no chance against the crop! Well, what ramifications does this have for our health? Do you notice a rise in auto-immune diseases? Cancer? Fatty livers? AHHH!!! We aren't sure just how bad it can become, but some issues are precancerous cell growth in the digestive tract, inhibited development of the brain, liver and testicles, partial atrophy of the liver, enlarged pancreas and intestines and immune system damage. My suggestion is to only use Organic Tamari Sauce. Tamari is a premium Japanese soy sauce. The major difference between Tamari and regular soy sauce is the proportion of ingredients between soybeans and wheat. While regular soy sauce contains 40-60% wheat, Organic Gluten Free Tamari is made with 100% soybeans and no wheat. While the sodium level of Tamari and regular soy sauce is the same, the higher concentration of soybeans in Tamari gives a richer, smoother, more complex taste than ordinary soy sauce.

Tamari is naturally fermented for up to 6 months and it doesn't contain MSG or artificial preservatives. Organic Gluten Free Tamari's fermentation process is different than ordinary soy sauce, giving it unique flavor enhancing properties. Add Tamari to gravies, sauces and casseroles. Use it as a marinade and in stir-fry dishes. Reduce sodium levels in your cooking without compromising taste. One teaspoon of Organic Tamari contains one-eighth the sodium as one teaspoon of salt.

Coconut Aminos are also a great soy sauce replacement. This delectably delicious soy-free sauce, containing 17 amino acids, is dark, rich, and salty. I am amazed at its resemblance to soy sauce. It is made simply from raw coconut tree sap and sun-dried sea salt, and naturally aged. This sap is very low glycemic (GI of only 35), is an abundant source of amino acids, minerals, vitamin C, broad-spectrum B vitamins, and has a nearly neutral PH. The majority of conventional soy sauces on the market are made with non-organic, genetically modified (GMO) soybeans. Long term use of unfermented soy-related products has led to an increase in soy allergies, a disruption in proper thyroid function, and an overload of estrogens in the body.

Coconut Aminos works great in dressings, marinades, sautés, and with sushi.

Tamari Sauce...

A richer, smoother, more complex taste

than ordinary soy sauce. Buy only organic.

A savory recipe made to love...

See next page.

Veggie Lo Mein with Poached Egg

Ingredients:

2 packages Miracle Noodles
1/4 c. coconut oil
2 c. fresh sliced mushrooms
1 c. broccoli
1/2 c. sliced bell peppers
1 onion, chopped
2 cloves garlic, minced
2 c. fresh bean sprouts
1/2 c. chopped green onions
1/4 tsp xanthan gum or guar gum
    or psyllium powder (thickener)
1 c. chicken broth
1 tsp sesame seed oil
2 tsp seasoned rice vinegar
1 TBS almond butter or
    macadamia nut butter
2 TBS Nature's Hollow honey or Swerve
1 TBS organic Tamari sauce (soy sauce)
1 tsp grated fresh ginger
1/4 tsp cayenne pepper
1/4 tsp curry powder

Directions...

Rinse and drain Miracle Noodles and set aside. Heat oil in a large wok or sauté pan. Stir fry mushrooms, broccoli, peppers, onion and garlic until tender. Stir in green onions and bean sprouts; cook one minute. Sift thickener into chicken broth in a small bowl and add to stir fry (sift in or it will clump up). Stir in sesame seed oil, rice vinegar, almond butter, sweetener, Tamari sauce, ginger, cayenne pepper and curry powder. Cook and stir until thickened and bubbly. Add Miracle Noodles, and toss. Serve with a poached egg or your favorite protein.

Makes 4 servings.
NUTRITIONAL COMPARISON (per serving)

Traditional Lo Mein =
490 calories, 20g fat, 10g protein, 56g carbs, 2.3g fiber (53.7g effective carbs)

"Healthified" Lo Mein =
228 calories, 18g fat, 8.5g protein, 8g carbs, 2.3g fiber (5.7g effective carbs)

Moo Goo Gai Pan

Ingredients:

1 TBS coconut oil
1 c. sliced fresh mushrooms
2 c. chopped broccoli florets
1 (8 oz.) can sliced bamboo shoots, drained
1 (8 oz.) can sliced water chestnuts, drained
1 TBS coconut oil
2 cloves garlic, minced
1 lb skinless, boneless chicken breast, cut into strips
1/4 tsp xanthan gum or guar gum or psyllium powder (thickener)
1 TBS Swerve
1 TBS organic Tamari (soy) sauce
1 TBS fish sauce
1 TBS rice wine
1/4 c. chicken broth

Directions...

Heat 1 tablespoon of oil in a wok or large skillet over high heat until it begins to smoke. Stir in the fresh mushrooms, broccoli, bamboo shoots. and water chestnuts. Cook and stir until all the vegetables are hot, and the broccoli is tender, about 5 minutes. Remove from the wok, and set aside. Wipe out the wok. Heat the remaining tablespoon of oil in the wok until it begins to smoke. Stir in the garlic, and cook for a few seconds until it turns golden-brown. Add the chicken, and cook until the chicken has lightly browned on the edges, and is no longer pink in the center, about 5 minutes. Stir together the thickener, sweetener, Tamari sauce, fish sauce, rice wine, and chicken broth in a small bowl. Pour over the chicken, and bring to a boil, stirring constantly. Boil for about 30 seconds until the sauce thickens and is no longer cloudy. Return the vegetables to the wok, and toss with the sauce. Serve with Miracle Rice or sautéed cauliflower rice.

Makes 3 servings.
NUTRITIONAL COMPARISON (per serving)
Traditional Moo Goo Gai Pan =
520 calories, 13g fat, 37g protein, 47g carbs, 2g fiber (45g effective carbs)
"Healthified" Moo Goo Gai Pan =
314 calories, 13g fat, 36.2g protein, 11g carbs, 4g fiber (7g effective carbs)

Turmeric FUN HERB FACT

This is one health boosting spice! It has been found to kill cancer cells, rejuvenate the liver, anti-inflammatory, helps decrease depression, decreases psoriasis and other inflammatory skin conditions

Malai Shrimp Curry

Ingredients:

16 shrimp
1 tsp chili powder
1/4 tsp turmeric powder
1 tsp Celtic sea salt, divided
3 TBS coconut oil
2 TBS Garlic paste
1 TBS Ginger paste
4 curry leaves, chopped
   (or 1/2 tsp curry powder)
1/2 c. onion, chopped
1 tomato, diced
1 red chili
2 tsp coriander powder
1 TBS Garam masala
1 tsp cumin powder
1 c. coconut milk
2 packages Miracle Rice

Directions...

Peel and clean the shrimp. Marinate shrimp with chili powder , turmeric and 1/2 tsp salt. Set aside. In a large pan heat oil. Add ginger-garlic, green chili, curry leaves and onions. Sauté onions till they become translucent. Add tomatoes, red chili, coriander, turmeric, garam masala, cumin and 1/2 tsp salt. Cook until a nice aroma and all the ingredients are well cooked. Add marinated shrimp, sauté until cooked through (about 4 minutes. Add the coconut milk and bring to boil. Serve over Miracle Rice and with "Healthified" Naan Bread.

Makes 4 servings. NUTRITIONAL COMPARISON (per serving)
Traditional Malai = 505 calories, 26g fat, 23g protein, 44.9g carbs, 2.9g fiber (42g effective carbs)
"Healthified" Malai = 336 calories, 25g fat, 21g protein, 7.8g carbs, 2.3g fiber (5.5g effective carbs)

"HEALTHIFIED" NAAN BREAD
3 eggs, separated
1/2 tsp cream of tartar
1/4 c. Jay Robb unflavored whey
3 oz. sour cream or coconut cream
OPTIONAL: 1 tsp curry powder

Separate the eggs (save the yolks for a different recipe), and whip the whites in a clean, dry, cool bowl for a few minutes until VERY stiff). Blend in the whey protein and sour cream (or softened coconut cream).

Heat the oil in a fry pan on medium high until a drop of water will sizzle. Once it is hot, place a circle of dough on the pan. Fry until golden brown on both sides. Remove from heat and place on a plate. Enjoy!

Makes 3 servings. NUTRITIONAL COMPARISON (per serving)
Traditional Naan Bread =
312 calories, 2.8g fat, 3.4g protein, 46g carbs, 1.9g fiber (44.1g effective carbs)
"Healthified" Fry Bread =
162 calories, 10.4g fat, 15.4g protein, 2.2g carbs, 0g fiber (2.2g effective carbs)

Why Weight Loss Gets Harder

Losing weight gets harder each time! Why, you ask? Well, a healthy liver is the main organ that governs fat loss. It processes hormones, cleanses the cells of toxins, makes cholesterol, breaks down fats, metabolizes carbohydrates and proteins, as well as many other bodily functions. When a liver is constantly stressed by dieting, it gets tired and toxic, which makes it unable to assist you in your weight loss journey. Not only that, but in Chinese medicine, they consider the liver function to govern our emotions. When the liver is stressed by poor food, alcohol, fructose and sugar, lack of sleep, or pollution, you are most likely to be depressed, anxious or angry. Low liver function causes food cravings, binge eating and excretion of too much cortisol.... causing more liver stress... It is a vicious cycle! Not to mention, if you go on anti depressants because your liver is causing low moods, the anti depressant causes more toxicity to your liver, which causes more depression and inability to lose weight.

The term "leaky gut" refers to when waste and partially digested foods are allowed into the blood stream due to perforations in the intestinal wall. People who are very sensitive to food poisoning have weak intestinal walls which allow bacteria to enter the blood easily. People who take antacids allow food particles to sit in their digestive system too long causing stress on the intestinal wall and are subject to leaky gut. This all causes water retention and stress on the liver. Some clients gain about 10-15 pounds of extra fluids. A healthy body is about 2/3rds water (hydrated cells are happy cells!) but when you have a leaky gut, water gets trapped and is unable to filter out toxins and waste; this also inhibits cell functions including the movement of fat. This is where cellulite comes into play. Your lymphatic system gets overwhelmed which causes the undesired effect of cellulite.

Also, our body and fat cells want to stay at "homeostasis"... when you lose weight, your fat cells shrink. When this happens, one of the 25 messengers in the fat cells sends powerful messages to the brain to eat. This message often sends people into an over-feeding binge, making the fat cells even larger and makes your set point even higher. Yo-yo dieting is very detrimental to fat cell growth.

Another important role is the liver ensures proper hormone balance. Estrogen dominance is a very common issue I see with many clients. First off it is because we are exposed to unhealthy external estrogen (such as non-organic meat and milk, alcohol, fructose, microwaving in plastics, drinking from plastic water bottles, and even soap leaches estrogens into the blood). But estrogens are detoxed by a healthy liver. Disruptions of the liver detoxification contributes to estrogen dominance; this causes difficulty in losing belly fat. Too often we are told to calculate calories in and calories out for weight loss. I believe it is all about hormone regulation. Insulin, estrogen, testosterone, leptin, ghrelin, glucagon, thyroid, progesterone, cortisol, human growth hormone as well as others determine our rate of fat metabolism, cravings, energy, sleep...if we fail to support our hormones, you can run all day and eat 500 calories and you will be frustrated at the conventional wisdom of the calorie lies.

The liver also produces over half of your bodies cholesterol production. Most of this is used to produce bile which breaks down fat. Bile gets stored in the gallbladder and is used to digest food and bile salts stimulate the secretion of water into the large intestine which helps us with proper bowel movements. One sign of a tired liver is that you don't have a daily bowel movement. Other signs are excess belly fat, fatty cysts, and age spots.

Signs of liver stress:
1. Chronic indigestion
2. Constipation
3. Cellulite
4. Hot feet at night
5. PMS or menopausal symptoms
6. Low moods: depression/anxious/irritable
7. You are negative or resentful
8. Muscle or joint pain
9. Headaches or migraines
10. Fatigued

The good news is, the liver can heal very rapidly when provided the right food and nutrients! I have a whole chapter on Liver Cleansing foods in my book: Secrets to a Healthy Metabolism. Instead of bogging down your liver with a high carb foods, try "healthified" recipes instead! Happy Eating!

Cheesy "Risotto"

Ingredients:

2 packages Miracle Rice
CHEESE SAUCE
1/4 c. butter
3 TBS Cream Cheese
1/4 c. beef/chicken broth
1 c. sharp cheddar cheese, shredded
1/4 c. Parmesan cheese, shredded
Sea salt and pepper (to taste)

Directions...Drain and rinse Miracle Rice in a strainer. Set aside.

In a saucepan, melt butter over medium heat until "browned" not black (this gives the butter an amazing flavor). Whisk in cream cheese; once well incorporated, add in the broth. Cook and stir for 2 minutes or until thickened. Reduce heat. Add the cheeses, stirring until cheese is melted. Add salt and pepper to taste. Pour over Miracle Rice.

Makes 4 servings.
NUTRITIONAL COMPARISON (per serving)

Traditional Cheese Risotto =
419 calories, 25g fat, 13g protein, 38g carbs, trace fiber (38g effective carb)

"Healthified" Cheese Risotto =
269 calories, 25g fat, 10.1g protein, 0.8g carbs, trace fiber (0.8g effective carbs)

Glucagon and Weight

I'd like to introduce you to an awesome fat-burning hormone called glucagon. Don't confuse this with glycogen. Glycogen is stored sugar in the muscles and liver; increasing insulin. Glucagon is the opposite hormone to insulin. Insulin takes sugars and carbohydrates you eat and stores it as fat. Glucagon takes the stored fat and breaks it down into sugar, creating a "fat burning" response. Do I have you intrigued?

In the presence of insulin, you can't burn fat for energy. Eating the typical American diet of sugar, fat-free and refined carbohydrates, stops fat burning. Overeating of any food will also increase insulin. Not only does this prevent fat burning, it also activates the storage of fat to make triglycerides and increasing LDL cholesterol. While many people believe their cholesterol problems derive from consuming fats and cholesterol, inflammation-causing carbohydrates are actually the source of these, and a variety of other health problems.

People wonder why I never suggest fat-free foods. Well, adding fat to your meal can actually slow the insulin response. If you added butter to your bread, it would cause less insulin response than eating the bread alone. Even ice cream with all its fat is less harmful to our waistline than eating the pure sugar alone, but I'm not recommending this. With blood sugar imbalances, mood is easily affected. High blood sugar levels cause fatigue and brain fog, like after a Thanksgiving meal. On the flip side, blood sugar levels that are too low can make you feel irritable, depressed, moody, or worried, which you may have felt an hour after eating candy or after skipping a meal. Conversely, when glucagon is stimulated, you will burn fat. There are several actions you can take to release this hormone. The first is eating adequate amounts of protein. This is why many of the high-protein diets work for people. There is a catch though, if you have liver damage or consume a lot of alcohol; which is a fat-storing carbohydrate anyway, your body can't burn protein efficiently. Glucagon works inside the liver, so for a person who has a healthy liver, eating protein is fat-burning, and consuming carbohydrate is fat-storing. Glucagon is also stimulated with exercise. Exercise increases glucagon up to 5 times our normal amounts! If you combine both exercise and increase amounts of protein, you can strategically enhance your weight loss.

Sushi Dinner
see page 121.

Chicken and Coconut "Rice"

Ingredients:

3 TBS coconut oil (melted) OR butter
1 1/2 TBS red wine vinegar
1 lime, juiced
1 tsp chili powder
1/2 tsp paprika
1/2 tsp onion powder
1/2 tsp garlic powder
1/2 tsp cayenne pepper
Sea salt and freshly ground black pepper to taste
1 lb chicken breast - cut into 1 1/2 inch cubes

OPTION:
Non-starchy Veggies for grill: Peppers, mushrooms, zucchini

RICE:
4 c. cauliflower, grated
1 TBS coconut oil OR butter
1/2 crumbled bouillon cube
   (watch out for MSG and gluten)

Directions...
In a small bowl, whisk together the oil, vinegar, and lime juice. Season with chili powder, paprika, onion powder, garlic powder, cayenne pepper, salt, and black pepper. Place the chicken in a shallow baking dish with the sauce, and stir to coat. Cover, and marinate in the refrigerator at least 1 hour. Preheat the grill for medium-high heat. Thread chicken onto skewers, and discard marinade. Lightly oil the grill grate. Grill skewers for 10 to 15 minutes, or until the chicken juices run clear.

"RICE": Place the cauliflower heads into a food processor and pulse until small pieces of 'rice.' Add oil to a pan over medium heat. Stir fry cauliflower for 2 to 3 minutes, add the crumbled bouillon cube over the "rice." Cook until just soft and serve with kabobs.

NUTRITIONAL COMPARISON (per serving)
Traditional Rice Kabobs =
567 calories, 16g fat, 39g protein, 59g carbs, 1.6g fiber (57.4g effective carbs)
"Healthified" Kabobs =
325 calories, 16g fat, 37.5g protein, 6.5g carbs, 2.9g fiber (3.6g effective carbs)

Busy Mom Tip:
I make a huge batch of cauliflower rice and keep it in the fridge for an easy addition to dinner when I am running late.

Southwestern Tabbouleh

Ingredients:

3 c. cauliflower
1/4 c. coconut oil or butter
1 c. chopped fresh cilantro
1 c. sliced red onion
3/4 c. diced tomato
1/2 c. sliced green onions
1/2 c. diced yellow pepper
1/2 c. chopped peeled avocado
1/4 c. diced seeded peeled cucumber
1/4 c. (1 oz.) crumbled queso fresco
2 TBS fresh lemon juice

2 TBS fresh lime juice
2 tsp diced seeded jalapeño
   pepper (optional)
3/4 tsp dried oregano
1/2 tsp Celtic sea salt
1/4 tsp ground cumin
1/4 tsp ground red pepper
1/4 tsp paprika
1/4 tsp chili powder
1/4 tsp freshly ground black pepper
1/8 tsp ground allspice
1 garlic clove, minced
Dash of hot pepper sauce
   (such as Tabasco)

Directions...

"RICE": Place the cauliflower heads into a food processor, pulse until small pieces of 'rice.' Place cauliflower rice in a frying pan with oil and stir fry until tender. Add cilantro and remaining ingredients; toss well. Fry for another 3-5 minutes to let the flavors soak into the cauliflower and enjoy!

Makes 4 servings. NUTRITIONAL COMPARISON (per serving)
Traditional Tabbouleh = 690 calories, 19g fat, 16g protein, 111.5g carbs, 7g fiber (104.5g effective carbs)
"Healthified" Tabbouleh = 229 calories, 17g fat, 5.5g protein, 13g carbs, 5.4g fiber (7.6g effective carbs)

Seafood "Risotto"

Ingredients:

1 head cauliflower
2 TBS coconut oil (or butter)
1/8 c. onion, diced
1 garlic clove, chopped fine
Celtic sea salt & pepper (to taste)
1/2 c. mascarpone cheese (or cream cheese)
1/2 c. chicken broth
1/4 c. grated parmesan cheese
1/2 c. prepared lobster or shrimp

Directions...

To make the Cauliflower "Rice," place the cauliflower pieces into a food processor grind the fresh cauliflower until it is rice size and set aside. Sauté the onion and garlic in the oil in a frying pan. Add "rice", salt & pepper, mascarpone and broth. Cook until it starts to reduce approximately 8 minutes, add Parmesan cheese and lobster; stir. Voila, you're done. Very easy. This makes a great hearty main course dish. To watch me making this on a local TV show, go to: http://www.kare11.com/news/news_article.aspx?storyid=901257

SUBSTITUTIONS: I like to mix it up and use different vegetables, or add meat like shrimp or chicken. Just keep all the basics the same, try making it with asparagus or mushrooms.

Makes 4 servings. NUTRITIONAL COMPARISON (per serving)
Traditional Risotto = 226 calories, 8.2g fat, 8.9g protein, 40g carbs, 1g fiber (39g effective carbs)
"Healthified" Risotto = 143 calories, 8.2g fat, 8.9g protein, 10.9g carbs, 4.1g fiber (6.8g effective carbs)

Mushroom "Risotto"

Ingredients:

4 1/2 c. Cauliflower, "riced"
1/2 c. chicken broth, divided
3 TBS coconut oil or butter, divided
1 pound portobello mushrooms, thinly sliced
1 pound white mushrooms, thinly sliced

2 shallots, diced
4 TBS butter
3 TBS finely chopped chives
Celtic sea salt to taste
freshly ground black pepper to taste
1/3 c. freshly grated Parmesan cheese

Directions...
Place cauliflower flowerets in a food processor and pulse until small pieces of "rice" (or use a cheese grater). In a saucepan, warm the broth over low heat. Heat 2 tablespoons oil in a large saucepan over medium-high heat. Stir in the mushrooms, and cook until soft, about 3 minutes. Remove mushrooms and their liquid, and set aside. Add 1 tablespoon oil to skillet, and stir in the shallots. Cook 1 minute. Add cauliflower rice, stirring to coat with oil, about 2 minutes. Add 1/2 cup broth to the "rice," and stir until the broth is absorbed. Stirring, until the liquid is absorbed, about 5 minutes. Remove from heat, and stir in mushrooms with their liquid, butter, chives, and parmesan. Season with salt and pepper to taste.

Makes 4 servings. NUTRITIONAL COMPARISON:
Traditional Risotto = 438 calories, 17.1g fat, 11.9g protein, 56.9g carbs, 2.7g fiber (54.2g effective carbs)
"Healthified" Risotto = 264 calories, 17.1g fat, 11.9g protein, 13.5g carbs, 5.1g fiber (8.4g effective carbs)

Paella

Ingredients:

MARINADE:
2 TBS macadamia nut or olive oil
1 TBS paprika
2 tsp dried oregano
Celtic sea salt and fresh black pepper to taste
2 lbs boneless chicken breasts, cut into 2 inch pieces

"RICE":
1 head of cauliflower, pulsed into "RICE"
4 TBS coconut oil, divided
3 cloves garlic, crushed
1 tsp crushed red pepper flakes
1 pinch saffron threads
1 bay leaf 1/2 bunch Italian flat leaf parsley, chopped
2 lemons, zested
1/2 c. onion, chopped
1 red bell pepper, coarsely chopped
1 lb chorizo sausage, casings removed and crumbled
1 lb shrimp, peeled and de-veined

Directions...
In a medium bowl, mix together 2 tablespoons oil, paprika, oregano, and salt and pepper. Stir in chicken pieces to coat. Cover, and refrigerate. Cut the cauliflower into pieces and pulse in a food processor until small pieces of "rice." TIP: You can also use the heart of the cauliflower for rice, or use for making "French Fries." Set aside "rice." (TIP: can do this up to 2 days ahead of time and store in fridge for easy lunch/dinner options). Heat 2 TBS oil in a large skillet or paella pan over medium heat. Stir in garlic, red pepper flakes, and Stir in saffron threads, bay leaf, parsley, lemon zest and cauliflower "rice". Cook, stirring, about 3-5 minutes or until cauliflower pieces are done to desired liking. Meanwhile, heat 2 tablespoons oil in a separate skillet over medium heat. Stir in marinated chicken and onion; cook 5 minutes. Stir in bell pepper and sausage; cook 5 minutes. Stir in shrimp; cook, turning the shrimp, until both sides are pink. Spread cauliflower "rice" mixture onto a serving tray. Top with meat and seafood mixture.

Makes 8 servings. NUTRITIONAL COMPARISON (per serving)
Traditional Paella = 736 calories, 35g fat, 55g protein, 46g carbs, 2.9g fiber (43.1g effective carbs)
"Healthified" Paella = 531 calories, 32g fat, 55g protein, 3.8g carbs, 1.3g fiber (2.3g effective carbs)

Shrimp Scampi

Ingredients:

1/2 c. butter or macadamia nut oil
1 TBS prepared Dijon-style mustard
1 TBS fresh lemon juice
1 TBS chopped garlic
1 TBS chopped fresh parsley
1 lb medium raw shrimp
1 bag Kelp Noodles

HELPFUL HINT:
For the Kelp noodles: put
them in a crockpot on low for
5-6 hours to make them soft.

Directions...

Prepare the Kelp Noodles according to directions (this only takes a minute... so less time in the kitchen! Yahoo!!!). Set aside in a beautiful serving dish.

Preheat oven to 450 degrees F. In a small saucepan over medium heat, combine the butter, mustard, lemon juice, garlic, and parsley. When the butter melts completely, remove from heat. Arrange shrimp in a shallow baking dish. Pour the butter mixture over the shrimp. Bake in preheated oven for 12 to 15 minutes or until the shrimp are pink and opaque. Place baked shrimp and butter sauce over the noodles and enjoy! Serve with "Healthified" Protein Garlic Bread (see pg. 100).

Makes 4 servings.
NUTRITIONAL COMPARISON (per serving)
Traditional Scampi (using gluten free RICE NOODLES) =
512 calories, 24g fat, 25g protein, 45g carbs, 1g fiber (44g effective carbs)
"Healthified" Scampi =
320 calories, 24g fat, 24.1g protein, 1.1g carb, 0g fiber (1.1g effective carbs)

Parsley
FUN HERB FACT

Diuretic herbs such as parsley prevent problems such as kidney stones and bladder infections and keep our body's plumbing running smoothly by causing it to produce more urine.

Coconut-Lime Fried "Rice"

Ingredients:

SAUCE
1/4 c. lime juice
2 TBS organic Tamari (soy sauce)
1/2 tsp stevia glycerite
1 TBS grated lime peel

"RICE"
1/2 c. unsweetened coconut flakes
2 TBS coconut oil, divided
3 eggs, beaten
1 TBS minced fresh ginger
1 1/2 c. chopped zucchini
4 c. cauliflower "rice"
1/4 c. chopped cilantro
1/2 c. macadamia nuts, coarsely chopped

Directions...

SAUCE: Combine all sauce ingredients in small bowl. Set aside.

"RICE": Place the cauliflower heads into a food processor, pulse until small pieces of 'rice.' Set aside.

Add 1 TBS of the oil to skillet; stir-fry eggs over medium heat 1 to 2 minutes or until scrambled but still moist. Remove eggs. Add remaining 1 tablespoon oil and ginger to skillet; stir-fry 40 to 60 seconds or until fragrant. Add zucchini and cauliflower "rice". Increase heat to medium-high; stir-fry 2 to 3 minutes or until crisp-tender. Stir in sauce until combined. Stir in egg, cilantro, half of the nuts and half of the coconut. Serve topped with remaining nuts and coconut.

Makes 6 servings.
NUTRITIONAL COMPARISON (per serving)

Traditional Fried Rice =
390 calories, 12g fat, 9g protein, 61g carbs, 2g fiber (59g effective carbs)
"Healthified" Fried Rice =
220 calories, 19.8g fat, 6.3g protein, 7.3g carbs, 3.1g fiber (4.2g effective carbs)

Cilantro
FUN HERB FACT

The carboxylic acid in cilantro binds to heavy metals such as mercury in the blood and carries them out of the body. Their removal reverses the toxin buildup that causes chronic fatigue, joint pain and depression.

Ketones

When you hear the words "butter" or "coconut oil" you have been trained to think "heart disease!" Well, I am here to tell you we have been replacing these natural good-mood fats with rancid vegetable oils (corn/canola/soybean) overloaded with omega 6 fats. Butter and coconut oil, actually protect the omega-3s in our brain. Outside of mother's milk, coconut oil is nature's richest source of medium chain triglycerides (MCT); they are extraordinary fats because they are not processed by your body in the same manner as long chain triglycerides. Coconut oil increases thermogenesis, which increases metabolism and produces energy. The medium chain fats in coconut oil goes directly to the liver and are immediately converted to energy, we call these KETONES. It also increases metabolism because it is easily absorbed and produces organelles in our cells. We have studied cows and other animals with different fats:

If you feed animals vegetable oils = put on weight and produce fatty meat
If you feed them coconut oil = very lean

Normal fat metabolism depends on bile salts that have been released from your gallbladder before being broken down in your digestive system. Coconut oil bypasses bile metabolism and goes directly to your liver where it is converted into ketones. The liver immediately releases KETONES into the bloodstream where they are transported to the brain to be used as fuel.

BENEFITS OF KETONES:

Ketones = stable source of energy for the brain during periods of low blood sugar without the harmful neurological side effects associated with high blood sugar.
Ketones = preferred source of brain food in people affected by diabetes or any neurodegenerative condition such as Alzheimer's, ALS, Parkinson's, & Multiple Sclerosis. In these conditions, the brain can no longer use glucose for fuel so we need to use an alternative source...ketones!
Ketones = help heart patients recover from a heart attack and they can dramatically shrink cancerous tumors.

So let's use some flavorful coconut oil to help our brain and body!

Scallops on Coconut "Rice"

Ingredients:

1 c. unsweetened coconut milk
2 TBS fresh lime juice
4 tsp fresh ginger, grated
2 garlic cloves, pressed
1 tsp fish sauce

2 tsp minced green chiles
2 TBS cilantro
2 TBS minced green onions
4 c. cauliflower, into "rice"
1 lb of scallops
2 tsp coconut oil
2 tsp butter
Celtic sea salt and pepper

Directions...

SAUCE: In a medium skillet, combine first 6 ingredients. Boil until sauce thickens slightly and is reduced to generous 3/4 cup, 8 to 9 minutes. Remove from heat; stir in cilantro and green onions. Season with salt and pepper.
"RICE": Place the cauliflower heads into a food processor, pulse until small pieces of 'rice.' Set on a plate and cover with sauce.
SCALLOPS: Rinse with cold water and thoroughly pat dry. Add the oil and butter to a 12 to 14-inch sauté pan on high heat. Salt and pepper the scallops. Once the oil and butter begins to smoke, gently add the scallops, making sure they are not touching each other. Sear the scallops for 1 1/2 minutes on each side. The scallops should have a 1/4-inch golden crust on each side while still being translucent in the center. Serve immediately over cauliflower risotto.

Makes 4 servings. NUTRITIONAL COMPARISON (per serving)
Traditional Risotto: 449 calories, 20g fat, 23g protein, 45g carbs, 2g fiber (43g effective carbs)
"Healthified" Risotto: 305 calories, 19g fat, 23g protein, 12g carbs, 4g fiber (8g effective carbs)

Shrimp with Lemon "Rice" and Crispy Basil

Ingredients:

SHRIMP:
16 jumbo shrimp
1 TBS ancho chile powder
1 1/2 tsp garlic salt
1 tsp ground coriander
1 tsp dried oregano
1/2 tsp ground cumin
1/2 tsp pepper
1-2 TBS coconut oil or ghee

LEMON RICE:
4 c. Cauliflower rice
1 large zucchini, trimmed,
    seeded, and diced, optional
1 1/2 TBS coconut oil or butter
1/2 c. finely diced onions
1 clove garlic, minced
1/4 c. chicken stock
1/4 c. fresh lemon juice
1 1/2 tsp Celtic sea salt plus
    more to taste
1/4 tsp freshly ground black pepper
plus more to taste

FRIED BASIL:
1 c. coconut oil or ghee
1 large bunch fresh basil,
    leaves only, well washed and dried

Directions...

SHRIMP: Rinse the shrimp under cold running water. Place the chile powder, garlic salt, coriander, oregano, cumin, and pepper in a mixing bowl and whisk to mix. Add the shrimp and toss to coat. Let the shrimp marinate in the refrigerator, covered, for 30 minutes to 1 hour. Put coconut oil and preheat pan to medium-high heat. When the pan is hot a drop of water will skitter in the pan. When ready to cook, place the marinated shrimp in the hot pan. They will be done after cooking 1 to 3 minutes per side. When done the shrimp will turn pinkish white and will feel firm to the touch.

LEMON RICE: Place cauliflower flowerets in a food processor. Pulse until small pieces of "rice." Heat the oil in a medium saucepan over medium heat. Add the onions and allow them to sweat their liquid for 4 minutes. Add the garlic and sweat for an additional 3 minutes. Stir in the "rice" and zucchini and sauté it for 3 minutes. Add the stock, lemon juice, salt, and pepper. Simmer for 10 minutes, or until the "rice" has absorbed most of the liquid.

FRIED BASIL: Heat the oil to 350 degrees F on a candy thermometer in a large saucepan over high heat. Standing as far back from the pot as possible and wearing an oven mitt, drop the basil leaves into the hot oil. The oil may bubble and splatter. Fry for about 1 minute, or until the leaves are crisp. Using a slotted spoon, transfer the leaves to a double layer of paper towels to drain. Adapted from Epicurious.com

NUTRITIONAL COMPARISON:
White Rice = 242 calories, 53 carbs, 0 fiber (53g effective carbs)
Brown Rice = 218 calories, 46 carbs, 4 fiber (42g effective carbs)
Quinoa = 222 calories, 39 carbs, 5 fiber (34g effective carbs)
Wild Rice = 166 calories, 35 carbs, 3 fiber (32g effective carbs)
Cauliflower Rice = 28 calories, 3 carbs, 1 fiber (2g effective carbs)

Rice and Inflammation

Yes, rice is "gluten-free." But I have a few reasons why our family doesn't eat it. First off, it will still cause inflammation and weight gain. The initial indicator of almost every illness is inflammation of our cells. Therefore it is critical for us to get a better understanding of what causes inflammation and choose the right foods to prevent it from happening!

Inflammation is usually associated with pain, swelling, and heat. BUT it doesn't always show externally; "silent inflammation" is more dangerous because we usually don't know we have it until an illness falls upon us. Everyday issues like headaches, sinus problems, allergies, skin disorders, acne, heart disease, stroke, aching joints and back, arthritis and cough are nothing more than a physical manifestation of silent inflammation. By the time we notice and address the symptoms, our cells have already been inflamed for a long time.

One of the reasons so many people are dealing with inflammation is because of a rapid rise in blood sugar, which causes biochemical changes in the cell. Choosing low-carbohydrate foods is one of the best ways to decrease inflammation. When blood sugar rises, sugar attaches to collagen in a process called "glycosylation", increasing inflammation (and increasing wrinkles!). Athletes also mistakenly eat too many carbohydrates that hinder their healing and recovery time because they are constantly inflaming their joints.

So, when I tell clients to eat "gluten free" they often grab all the "gluten-free" pre-packaged foods on the shelf…but that most likely will cause weight gain and slow the healing process in your gut. Rice flour, the common flour substitute in gluten-free products, is higher in calories, higher in carbohydrates, and lower in nutrients than regular flour. It can cause more inflammation in our body. So my recommendation is to make your own healthier options by using almond flour and coconut flour, which are very easy to digest. The healthy fats in nuts are actually nourishing to our brain.

Using high quality fats is also essential to reduce inflammation in the body. Omega-6 fats, found in margarine, soybean, corn and safflower oils, are inflammation-causing fats; these are found in salad dressings, most pre-made pesto sauces, Jiff peanut butter, ALL pre-packaged cookies and crackers, frozen dinners… In contrast, omega-3 fats, found in fish (sardines, anchovies, salmon), vegetables, grass-fed butter, and free range eggs, have an inflammation-suppressing effect. Gamma-linolenic acid (GLA) is a healthy omega-6 fat that enhances the anti- inflammatory effect of omega-3 fats. Both GLA and omega-3 fish oils are helpful in healing arthritis, eczema, and other inflammatory issues. GLA is found in leafy green vegetables, olive oil, walnut oil, macadamia oil, avocados and nut butters.

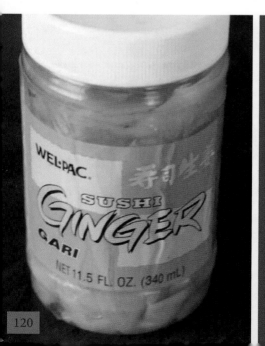

You wouldn't think that something like pink pickled ginger at your favorite sushi restaurant would be harmful, but it has aspartame (an excito-toxin that causes your brain neurotransmitters to malfunction and causes you to eat uncontrollably) and it has food dye. Yep, pickled ginger should be white!

QUICK TIP:
To get nice cuts of sushi clean the knife and wet it before each cut. This will keep the knife from sticking as you cut.

Sushi

Ingredients:

4 c. cauliflower rice
2 TBS cream cheese softened
    (or 2 TBS coconut oil)
1 cucumber
1 avocado
Nori seaweed sheets
Sesame seeds (black or white)
Wasabi paste
Coconut aminos
Pickled ginger

VARIATION 1
(California Rolls)
4 oz. crab meat

VARIATION 2
(Smoked salmon roll)
4 oz. naturally smoked salmon
4 oz. cream cheese

VARIATION 3
(Rainbow roll)
4 oz. of sushi grade fish
    (Salmon, Tuna, etc)

SPICY MAYO:
1 TBS mayonnaise
1 tsp hot sauce

Directions...
Make cauliflower rice per instructions on page 113. Let it cool and mix in cream cheese or coconut oil (to help bind the rice together).

Cut cucumber and avocado into long strips about a quarter of an inch at widest point. Place nori sheet on cutting board (or on a bamboo mat to help with forming and rolling). Starting at one edge of the nori sheet press a thin layer of cauliflower rice onto the sheet. If doing a "normal" roll (rice on the inside) leave a half inch of nori without any rice on it. If making an inside out roll (rice on the outside) fill nori sheet with rice and carefully flip it over so rice side is down.

CALIFORNIA ROLL:
Follow directions for a normal roll. About 1/2-inch from the top edge of nori, place a row of cucumber, a row of avocado and a row of crab meat. Carefully roll the sushi as far as the inch of nori that has no rice on it. Wet this part of the nori and seal the roll shut. You can use the bamboo mat to help shape the roll. Using a very sharp knife, cut the roll into 1 inch long pieces.

SMOKED SALMON ROLL:
Follow directions for normal roll. About a half inch from the top edge of nori, place a row of cucumber, and a row of smoked salmon. Cut cream cheese into 1-inch long by 1/4-inch square pieces and place a row along the salmon. Carefully roll the sushi as far as the inch of nori that has no rice on it. Wet this part of the nori and seal the roll shut. You can use the bamboo mat to help shape the roll. Using a very sharp knife, cut the roll into 1-inch long pieces.

RAINBOW ROLL:
Follow directions for inside out roll. About half an inch from the top edge of the nori, place a row of cucumber and a row of avocado. Carefully roll use the bamboo mat to aide in rolling and shaping (Alternately place 1 inch slices of fish and avocado onto outside of roll and press in place with bamboo mat). Using a very sharp knife, cut the roll into 1 inch long pieces.

Place pieces onto a plate and drizzle with spicy mayo. Sprinkle sesame seeds on top and serve with wasabi, pickled ginger and coconut aminos.

Makes 6 servings. NUTRITIONAL COMPARISON (per serving)
Traditional California Roll: 310 calories, 3.5g fat, 7g protein, 67g carbs, 1g fiber (66g effective carbs)
"Healthified" California Roll: 256 calories, 11.8g fat, 27.3g protein, 12.5g carbs, 6.6g fiber (5.9g effective carbs)

Recipe Index

Recipes in Alphabetical Order